EMP NESTERS

SERENDIPITY EXECUTIVE EDITOR:
Lyman Coleman

AUTHOR:
Keith Madsen

CARTOONIST:
Christopher Werner

LAYOUT PRODUCTION TEAM:
Sharon Penington
Erika Tiepel

MOVING ON TO THE SECOND HALF

Topics	Session	TRACK 1 LIFE STORIES	TRACK 2 BIBLE STUDY
ORIENTATION	1	Get Acquainted	
A NEW FREEDOM	2	Jim, Cynthia	
	3		Exodus 16:1–8
A NEW FAMILY ROLE	4	Ralph, Rhonda	
	5		Mark 3:20–21, 31–35
A NEW PURPOSE	6	Kevin, Ellen	
	7		Isaiah 49:1–6
A NEW MARRIAGE PARTNERSHIP	8	Ann, Virginia	
	9		Acts 18:1–3, 18–20, 24–26
A NEW SPIRITUALITY	10	Karl, Rose	
	11		Genesis 32:22–30
A NEW FUTURE	12	Sharon, Norm	
	13		Genesis 12:1–7

Serendipity House • P.O. Box 1012 • Littleton, CO 80160

TOLL FREE 1-800-525-9563

1/96

96 97 98 99 /CH/ 6 5 4 3 2 1

Beginning a Small Group

1. AGENDA: There are three parts to every group meeting.

GATHERING	STUDY	CARING
15 min.	30 min.	15–45 min.
Purpose:	Purpose: To	Purpose: To share
To break the ice	discuss the issue	your own needs

2. FEARLESS FOURSOME: If you have more than seven in your group at any time, call the option play when the time comes for Study, and subdivide into groups of 4 for greater participation. (In 4's, everyone will share and you can finish the Study in 30 minutes). Then regather the group for CARING.

GATHERING	STUDY	CARING
All Together	Groups of 4	Back Together

3. EMPTY CHAIR: Pull up an empty chair during CARING at the close and ask God to fill this chair each week. Remember, by breaking into groups of four for the Study time, you can grow numerically without feeling "too big" as a group.

The Group Leader needs an apprentice-in-training at all times so that the apprentice can start a new "cell" when the group size is 12 or more.

Questions about this course

DEFINITION

1. **What is this support group?** This support group is an intentional face-to-face gathering of 3 to 12 people on a regular time schedule with the common purpose of discovering and growing in the possibilities of the abundant life in Christ.

OPEN

2. **Can a person who is on their way back to God be in this support group?** Yes. That is what this group is all about. This group is for:

   • People who may be hesitant about the church but are looking for a spiritual faith.

   • People who are experiencing an "empty nest" and are looking to God for hope and new direction.

   • People who are crippled by a bad experience with the church and want to start over in their spiritual pilgrimage.

   • People who are down on themselves and need encouragement to see beyond their own shortcomings.

   • People who are looking for hope in the face of seemingly insurmountable difficulties.

   • People who flashed across your mind as you read over this list.

FIRST SESSION

3. **What will we do at the first meeting?** Part of the "Orientation" session is to get acquainted and to decide on the Ground Rules for your group. To keep the first session from going too long, members should read the Preface on page 6 later, or have the leader make the Preface into a short talk.

THREE

4. **What do we study for the rest of the course?** Your group has three basic options: (See the schedule in the Table of Contents.)

   • **Option One:** Track 1—Life Stories. A general discussion of the issue, including contemporary Life Stories.

   • **Option Two:** Track 2—Bible Study. A study on the issue, comparing your experience to a story from Scripture.

   • **Option Three:** Tracks 1 and 2 (for a total of 13 weeks rather than 7 weeks)—spending two sessions on each topic. If possible, we recommend that you choose this option so that your group can benefit from both Life Stories and Bible Study.

5. **What is the agenda for the sessions?** See page 2 for the three important parts to every group meeting. Page 2 also explains how to form groups of four for the Study segment of the meeting.

6. **How long is each small group session?** Sixty to 90 minutes, if you use the suggested times for each part of the session given in the book. You may have to pick and choose the questions that fit the needs and interests of the group.

7. **Who leads the meetings?** Anyone may guide these discussions. The leader doesn't have to be a teacher or counselor, but simply gets the group started and keeps it on track. One person can lead all the time, or you can rotate leadership among the members.

8. **What is at the heart of this group?** This is a support group. This is a group in which you can tell your stories. This is a group where you can learn together, pray together, laugh together, and, if necessary, cry together.

9. **What will NOT take place in this group?** This is not a therapy group. This is not a lecture by an expert. This is not group counseling. This is not a replacement for professional therapy.

**GROUND
RULES**
10. What are the ground rules for the group? You will have a chance to discuss expectations and ground rules during the first small group session on pages 14–15.

CONTINUING
11. What happens to the group after finishing the course? The group is free to disband or to continue. (See the fold-out description of the entire line of Serendipity small group materials in the center section of this book.) In Session 13, you will find various suggestions for continuing on as a group. Call Toll Free **1-800-525-9563** for suggestions about other courses and to receive a free Serendipity Resource Catalog.

PREFACE

It's a time many look forward to with eager anticipation. It's a time many approach with fear and regret. It's the time that last child has left the home, and a couple or single parent is left to themselves. It's the time of the "empty nest." How do we go about making the most of this life situation? That is what we will seek to do in this course.

As we seek for guidance, we really get little help from looking back to how people have approached this in the past, largely because the "empty nest" has not been part of life for a long time historically. The researchers who wrote *Lifetrends: The Future of Baby Boomers and Other Aging Americans*, point out, "... the existence of the 'empty nest' stage of family life is more recent than many people realize. In 1900, a 22-year-old woman who married would, on the average, become a widow at age 60 and die herself at age 64. Since it's likely that she would have had many children throughout her reproductive years, there is a good chance that her last child would still have been living at home at the time of her death."[1] Going back even further to biblical times, most parents kept their adult male children living with them, along with their daughters-in-law and their grandchildren. That certainly didn't make for an "empty nest"!

While history may not be much help, social research has highlighted some of the important issues of this time of life, and these are issues about which Scripture does have much to say. We will look in this study at a number of new things we can expect from life as we face the empty nest:

A New Freedom

There is no doubt about it—as much as we may love our children, they do tie us down. Our lives center around them from that first day we bring them home as an infant and they keep us up all night, through those days we are going 10 different directions trying to attend all their ballgames and recitals, to those times we stay up all night worrying because they are out late with that person we just don't trust. The empty nest brings the potential of a new freedom from those constraints, and for looking to our own interests. While this freedom can be a relief for many of us, it can also mean some adjustments. Christian counselor and radio talk-show host Jim Smoke has written, "Until now, it probably seemed there was a constant need, and it was always someone else's. Your children seemed to be continually marching toward you with outstretched arms and open hands, saying, 'I need! I need!' Now, for the most part, they're adults able to meet their own needs, and perhaps for the first time ... you feel free to focus on yourself and your own needs. But it takes some retraining of the brain to say out loud for the first time 'I need!' Most of us do not do well at this."[2] Will we be able to make the adaptations needed to get maximum benefit from this new freedom?

A New Family Role

When the last child moves out of the house, we don't lose our family, but rather we take on a new family role. That role can involve some or all of the following:

- GRANDPARENTING—A popular bumper sticker says, "If I had known how much fun grandchildren are, I would have had them first!" Certainly grandchildren can be fun. As a grandparent, you can usually enjoy your grandchildren without having to take the same level of responsibility and burden you did with your children. Usually that is the case—not always. Sometimes today, grandparents are forced into a more active role, either because parents are irresponsible, or because parents run into especially difficult circumstances, like health problems.

- CARING FOR ELDERLY PARENTS—Sometimes no sooner do we finish caring for our children than our parents become less able to care for themselves, and we must take a role in their care. Often this task falls to the woman of the household. Such care can mean anything from helping with cleaning and the more physically exhausting tasks of running a home, to having power of attorney, to constant nursing care of an invalid. Taking a parent or in-law into the home often brings a great deal of stress. In fact, a University of Michigan School of Nursing study showed that those caring for the aged suffered from depression three times as often as the older people they cared for."[3]

- SERVING AS A REFUGE TO ADULT CHILDREN IN STRESS— Adult children run into many kinds of stress—divorce and financial hardship in an increasingly tight economy are the two most common. In such times, we learn that our adult children are not quite as ready to be on their own as they, and we, once thought. Adult children may ask us for loans, or even for the chance to move back into our home "just for a while—until things get better." In 1980, according to the United States census, almost five hundred thousand divorced men and women in their 20s and three hundred thousand married couples lived with their parents.[4] What do we do if we are asked to fill such a role?

A New Purpose

For the first part of life a man's sense of purpose is closely linked to his paid work, and a woman's sense of purpose (at least traditionally) has been most closely linked to her role as a mother. In the second half of life all of that changes. A man starts to look toward retirement. What will give his life purpose and meaning when he is no longer paid to do a job? A woman no longer is called upon to care for young children. If she has not developed a career of her own, where will she find meaning and purpose?

Many people at this age find new purpose through volunteer work. Men and women employed outside the home may find that their paid work is just a paycheck, with little that brings satisfaction. Homemakers who are no longer preoccupied with parenting may find in volunteer work a new reason for being. Perhaps that is why a Gallup poll showed that between 1977 and 1986, the number of Americans who did volunteer work increased from 27 percent to 36 percent. College graduates over 50 did more of this unpaid labor than anyone else.[5]

A New Marriage Partnership

Counselor Jim Smoke notes that for many "empty nest" couples, their life had previously so centered around their children that when those children leave they wonder what they have in common with each other.[6] Marriage after the children leave can either be a time to discover a new intimacy, or it can be a time when a couple is forced to face the problems that they have with each other as a couple. Counselors William H. Bergquist, Elinor Miller Greenberg, and G. Alan Laum write, "When couples fail to develop a new intimacy in these years, the problem is usually they no longer have any common interests ... They discover new time together in their fifties but have nothing to share in that time."[7] Couples who develop new intimacy during this time, on the other hand, are those who, if they do not already have things they enjoy doing together, have gone out intentionally to find such activities. Maybe they both take up golf for the first time, or maybe they get involved in a community service project together.

In any case, marriage after the empty nest will probably not be what it was before, and the couple who wants the change to be an improvement would be well-advised to plan for it deliberately.

A New Spirituality

When you are young and first married, it's typical in our country to become preoccupied with the accumulation of things, and with driving toward a more prestigious position with higher pay. Empty nesters often have experienced enough of life to see that such pursuits do not ultimately satisfy, and they are looking for more. Counselor Jim Smoke writes, "I listen to more and more fifty-something men talk about their desire to deepen their relationship with God and walk closer to Him. Some are reconnecting after years of being disconnected. Others are seeking connection for the first time."[8] Freedom from parental responsibilities can provide the opportunity for spiritual enrichment for those who want to take advantage of it.

A New Future

At each stage of life a person has to make the decision, do I spend my time looking back at what I have lost, or do I look ahead to the new future that is in store for me? Certainly, we do lose something when our children go off on their own. We lose a role we have lived with for 20 or 30 years, and we put behind us a time when we nurtured young lives and had them constantly around to provide companionship. We have also lost our youth, and some mourn that as well. We are taught in our culture to idealize youth and fear aging as nothing more than a path toward death. But for those with their eyes open to the possibilities, our 40s, 50s and 60s provide new opportunities for self-exploration. We have often gained a wisdom and a self-confidence that we longed for in our younger years, and these can help us toward a life that is more fulfilling.

The time of the empty nest, then, will be what we make it. For those of us who look only at what we have lost, it will be a hard time. But for those of us who look at the new things this period of life brings to us, it will be a time of exciting opportunity. This study is aimed at helping that to happen for all of us.

NOTES:

[1] Jerry Gerber, Janet Wolff, Walter Klores and Gene Brown, *Lifetrends: The Future of Baby Boomers and Other Aging Americans* (New York: Macmillan, 1989), p. 21.
[2] Jim Smoke, *Facing 50: A View From the Mountaintop* (Nashville: Thomas Nelson Publishers, 1994), p.4.
[3] Gerber, et.al., p.24.
[4] Ibid., p. 22.
[5] Ibid., p. 84.
[6] Smoke, p. 35.
[7] Ibid., p. 38.
[8] Ibid., p. 87.

Orientation

PURPOSE

To get acquainted, to share your expectations and to decide on the ground rules for your group.

AGENDA

 Gathering   Study   Caring

OPEN

GATHERING / 15 Minutes / All Together

Leader: Give out name tags and have everyone introduce themselves. As everyone gives their names, jot down their name and phone number inside the front cover. Briefly, go over the "Questions about this course" on pages 3–5 and summarize the "Preface" on pages 6–9 in your own words. Then, ask everyone to turn to this page as you explain the 3-part agenda of each meeting: (1) Gathering—15 minutes; (2) Study—30 minutes, and (3) Caring—15–45 minutes. (If you have 90 minutes for the meeting, use the extra 30 minutes for Caring).

Start off by reading or asking for a volunteer to read the Introduction below. Then, use the Ice-Breaker to get acquainted.

INTRODUCTION

Welcome to this course on empty nesters! In the next few weeks, you will have a chance to talk about issues related to your family and adjusting to your new roles in life now that your children are gone (or will soon be going) from your home. You will also get to know each other and learn to support one another.

While this course refers to "empty" nesters, our emphasis will be less on what is "empty" in our life and more on what is full. When we have an open attitude, this time of life is full of new things—new opportunities, new freedom, and new purpose. But we must be prepared to take advantage of these new opportunities. This course will help us do that.

In this first session, you will have a chance to get acquainted and share a little of your own story. At the end of this session, you will have a chance to share your expectations and decide on the ground rules for this group.

You will also have to decide which track you want to follow in this course. (See schedule in the Table of Contents.) Track 1 is an introductory track—with life stories taken from contemporary life. Track 2 is a deeper track—with case studies taken from stories in the Bible. If you can give 13 weeks to this course, you can take both tracks—Track 1 the first week, Track 2 the next week.

In this first session, be sure to set aside at least 30 minutes at the close to make these decisions. Now, start with the Ice-Breaker. Call time after 15 minutes and move on to the Study.

Ice-Breaker. Use the questions below to get acquainted. Go around the group on the first question. Then go around on the next question.

1. Begin by sharing your name, how many children and grandchildren (if any) you have, and where those children live.

2. If you were to compare your family when your children were in grade school or junior high, to a family in a TV show or movie, which one would you compare it to?
   - ❐ Leave It to Beaver
   - ❐ The Simpsons
   - ❐ The Cosby Show
   - ❐ Father Knows Best
   - ❐ Home Improvement
   - ❐ Roseanne
   - ❐ The Waltons
   - ❐ The Addams Family
   - ❐ Married With Children
   - ❐ Home Alone
   - ❐ The Rocky Horror Picture Show

 STUDY / 30 Minutes / Groups of 4

Leader: If you have more than 7 in your group, we recommend that you move quickly into groups of 4 for this Study time (4 at the dining table, 4 at the kitchen table, etc.). In groups of 4, everyone can participate, and you can finish the Study in 30 minutes. Then, bring the entire group back together for the Caring time.

Life Stories. Have someone read out loud the stories of the two people below. Then discuss the questions which follow.

Carol
Carol had been a single mother for 10 years. During that time her daughter Erin had been the focus of her life and her chief companion. Carol got remarried when Erin was 14. When Erin got married herself at 20 it was very difficult for Carol. It became even more difficult when Carol's husband got a new job in a distant city, and she couldn't even see her daughter regularly. She called her almost every day and was depressed much of the time. Carol's husband began to feel that his presence was of secondary importance to Erin's absence.

Jake

Jake is a 46-year-old man who works as a printer for a large company in a major metropolitan area. He lives with his second wife, Mary, in a blue-collar suburb just outside the city. His two daughters are now grown and married. He has two grandchildren—a 2-year-old granddaughter and a 4-year-old grandson. Both of Jake's parents have been dead for quite a while. Mary's mother is still alive and lives with them.

Jake went to work for his present employer right after he graduated from high school. Lately, however, Jake's been feeling depressed and angry. He recognizes that he has advanced as far as possible in the company. But he knows that it would be risky for him to change jobs. Not only would he lose his seniority, but he couldn't really duplicate his fringe benefits at another company. And yet, Jake knows he doesn't want to do this job the rest of his working days. Often, when the presses are running, he will dream of being the owner of an upstate fishing resort.

DISCUSS

"A time for tears? A time for joy? It's a time for both ... and you will experience both. But it is also your time for a future of fulfillment after the empty nest."
—Cynthia P. Coad in *Your Full Future: After the Empty Nest*

Questions:

1. Which part of these people's stories sounds most like your own experience?
   - ❏ missing a child who has left the home, like Carol
   - ❏ feeling neglected because of my spouse's preoccupation with an absent adult child, like Carol's husband
   - ❏ having a mother-in-law move in with us, like Jake
   - ❏ feeling depressed about a dead-ended job, like Jake
   - ❏ none of this really sounds like my situation

2. Think back to the time when *you* first "left the nest." What was the most exciting thing to you about that transition? What was the scariest thing?

3. When your nest became empty, what else in your life did that leave empty or full? Mark each area:

OUR CHECKBOOK

Empty	1/4	1/2	3/4	Full

OUR CALENDAR

Empty	1/4	1/2	3/4	Full

MY HEART

Empty	1/4	1/2	3/4	Full

4. How open are you to looking to God to help you fill the empty spaces in your heart and life?
   ❐ I'm really not very "religious."
   ❐ I prefer to do things for myself.
   ❐ I'm open, but I don't know how.
   ❐ It hasn't helped so far.
   ❐ That's what I really need in my life.

CARING / 15–45 Minutes / All Together

Leader: Bring all of the groups back together for a time of caring. In this first session, you need to set the ground rules and goals for your group. Then close the meeting together with the Serenity Prayer.

INTRODUCTION

Now is the time to decide what you want to get out of this course. For yourself. For your group. And to agree on the ground rules for your group. Follow these steps.

Step One: EXPECTATIONS. Give everyone a chance to share two things that you would like to get out of this course and this group, starting with the following list:

❐ a closer walk with God
❐ an understanding of what a personal faith in Christ means
❐ to be in a small group where I can deal with the struggles I have
❐ to discover what my options are for the future
❐ to discover what God wants me to do with the rest of my life
❐ to get to know some other people like me
❐ to learn more about the Bible
❐ to learn how to pray
❐ to have fun
❐ to rethink my lifestyle, now that I have committed my life to Christ
❐ to find my niche in the church
❐ other_____

Step Two: GROUND RULES. What are some ground rules you would like to set for this group? See if you can agree on two or three.

❐ ATTENDANCE: Group members will give priority to the group meetings for 13 weeks or sessions unless you decide on using only Track 1 or 2. (See schedule in the Table of Contents.)

❏ QUESTIONS ENCOURAGED: This is a support group for people who are struggling with all sorts of questions, including questions about your spiritual faith. Honest questions are encouraged.

❏ MISSION: This group will be "open" to anyone who is struggling, and also to anyone who is seeking or who is starting over in the Christian life ... and it will be the mission of this group to invite new people to the sessions.

❏ ACCOUNTABILITY: This group will be a support group. Prayer requests will be shared at the end of every session and group members will be encouraged to call each other to ask, "How's it going?"

❏ ADVICE-GIVING: It is okay to offer advice to another group member, but only when it is requested.

❏ CONFIDENTIALITY: Anything that is said in the group is kept in confidence.

❏ COVENANT: At the end of this course, the group will evaluate the experience and decide if they wish to continue as a group.

PRAYER | **Step Three: SERENITY PRAYER.** Close your time by reading this prayer together:

"Dear God,
Grant us the serenity to accept
the things that we cannot control,
the courage to change the things we can,
and the wisdom to know the difference.
Amen."

REMINDER | If you know of someone who would benefit from this course, now is the time to invite them. Next session you will start on the first issue in this course. It would be quite easy for a new person to join your group next session.

HOMEWORK | Ask everyone to read the Preface on pages 6–9 before the next session.

DIRECTORY | If you have not already jotted down their names, pass around your books and have everyone write their names and phone numbers in the GROUP DIRECTORY inside the front cover.

<table>
<tr><td rowspan="2">SESSION
2</td><td colspan="2"><h1>A New Freedom</h1></td></tr>
<tr><td>LIFE STORIES</td><td>BIBLE STUDY</td></tr>
</table>

PURPOSE	To introduce the subject of "A New Freedom" and to continue the process of becoming a group.
AGENDA	Gathering Study Caring

OPEN

 GATHERING / 15 Minutes / All Together

Leader: Welcome any newcomers and explain the purpose of the course, the "ground rules" that you agreed upon in the last session and the three-part agenda for the meetings. Also, explain that this session is the first of two sessions on the issue of "A New Freedom."

Start off by reading the Introduction to the group or ask for a volunteer to read it. Then, use the Ice-Breaker to start the meeting. Remember to keep to the 3-part agenda.

NTRODUCTION

Life changes can generally either be seen as losses or as gains. For instance, when a daughter gets married the saying is, "You haven't lost a daughter; you've gained a son!" The empty nest is certainly that way. Some people might get down about what is now behind them. But how much better it is to see what we have gained! And at the center of what we have gained is the new freedom we have to pursue our own interests. One woman from Ohio, writing to the researchers who wrote *Lifetrends: The Future of Baby Boomers and Other Aging Americans*, noted that she and her husband "had never had it so good." She went on to say, "WE can make plans to fit OUR schedules, WE can plan meals (or eat out) as WE please, WE can impulsively stop on the way home from work, WE can go away for the weekend ... It's wonderful."[1]

This is the first of two sessions on the issue of "A New Freedom." Start off with the Ice-Breaker. Then, move into the Life Stories, and save time at the close for Caring. Caring is what this course is really all about.

Ice-Breaker. Go around the group on the first question. If you have time go around again on the next question.

1. If you were to choose equivalents of the "four basic food groups" to nourish your emotional well-being, ("religious" activities not included!) what would they be? (choose the top two)

    ☐ getting hugs from friends   ☐ watching my "soaps"
    ☐ professional success   ☐ having time alone
    ☐ shopping   ☐ watching sports on TV
    ☐ watching old movies   ☐ reading romance novels
    ☐ traveling   ☐ talking on the phone
    ☐ camping in the mountains   ☐ fishing
    ☐ listening to music   ☐ laying on the beach
    ☐ jogging   ☐ taking a walk
    ☐ playing with my grandchildren
    ☐ attention from the opposite sex
    ☐ other _____

2. Which of the above do you feel most "hungry" for right now?

STUDY / 30 Minutes / Groups of 4

Leader: If you have more than 7 in your group, we recommend that you move quickly into groups of 4 for the Study time (4 at the dining table, 4 at the kitchen table, etc.). In groups of 4, everyone can participate and you can finish the Study in 30 minutes. Then, bring the entire group back together for the Caring time.

Life Stories. Have someone read out loud the stories of the two people below. Then, use your own experience to discuss the questions which follow.

Jim

Jim had always wanted to take up golf. He loved the out-of-doors, and the somewhat easy pace of the game appealed to him, since he spent his working hours rushing around trying to meet deadlines. However, having children in the home had always meant that there was little money available for this rather expensive game. In addition, there never seemed to be time, since they were always heading off to his son's football or baseball games, or to watch their daughter play piano. Now that their son was married and their daughter in an out-of-state college, this had changed.

Cynthia

When Cynthia was a child, she used to dream of writing novels like Emily or Charlotte Bronte. She had always done well in English class, and her teacher in her senior year had even advised that she try to publish a story she wrote that year. She never did, but the dream stayed with her, even when she married two years later. The problem was that she never seemed to have time once she started raising her family. When the last of her three daughters left home to go to college she started looking at her dream again. It was a little scary—scary because now she knew she had no more excuses. What would happen if she tried and failed? She knew the fiction market was extremely competitive. She could put in a lot of work—not to mention the emotional investment—and never get a thing published. Freedom had given her an opportunity, but it was a two-edged sword.

DISCUSS | **Questions:**

1. Cynthia dreamed of being a writer when she was young. Where did you live in the seventh grade, and what did you dream of becoming?

2. What do you identify with most in the stories of the people above?
   - ❏ looking forward to playing more golf!—like Jim
   - ❏ having a job where I have to rush around to meet deadlines—like Jim
   - ❏ feeling my kids have kept me from pursuing my own recreational interests, like Jim
   - ❏ having a life-long dream, like Cynthia
   - ❏ feeling that having a family has kept me from fulfilling my dream, like Cynthia
   - ❏ being a little afraid of failing at my dream, like Cynthia
   - ❏ none of this relates much to me

3. Of the various kinds of freedom being an "empty nester" provides, which is most important to you?
   - ❏ freedom to pursue recreational interests
   - ❏ greater freedom from financial pressures
   - ❏ freedom to pursue my dreams
   - ❏ freedom from all that responsibility and worry
   - ❏ freedom to focus on us as a couple

4. Which of the following activities would you have an interest in pursuing, now that you have more freedom to do so? (Mark all that apply):

    ❏ golf
    ❏ writing
    ❏ getting into politics
    ❏ tracing my genealogy
    ❏ reading
    ❏ house remodeling
    ❏ fishing
    ❏ backpacking
    ❏ gourmet cooking
    ❏ artistic expression, like painting or music

    ❏ mountain-climbing
    ❏ traveling
    ❏ scuba diving
    ❏ making things out of wood
    ❏ being an entrepreneur
    ❏ volunteer work in the community
    ❏ volunteer work in the church
    ❏ aerobics/working out at the gym

    If you are here with your spouse, check to see what you both marked. Any surprises?

5. Cynthia had ambivalent feelings about being free to follow her dream. How are you feeling toward the freedom you have?
    ❏ Better to be "tied down" with children!
    ❏ What freedom?!
    ❏ It's a little frightening.
    ❏ It's boring.
    ❏ It's exhilarating.

6. What would help you enjoy the freedom you have more?
    ❏ having someone to share the activities I enjoy
    ❏ letting go of the past
    ❏ being encouraged by someone to follow my dream
    ❏ having someone to help me see the opportunities
    ❏ I'm using my freedom just fine right now, thank you!

 CARING / 15–45 Minutes / All Together

Leader: Regather all the groups for the Caring time. Start off with Sharing. Then, if you feel comfortable, move to a time for prayer requests.

SHARING

Take your pick of the special scriptural promises listed below. Which brings you the most meaning as you look at the challenges ahead of you? Tell the group why you chose the one you did.

Train a child in the way he should go, and when he is old he will not turn from it.
Proverbs 22:

Remember how the Lord your God led you all the way in the desert these forty years, to humble you and to test you in order to know what was in your heart, whether or not you would keep his commands.
Deuteronomy 8:2

"Forget the former things; do not dwell on the past. See, I am doing a new thing! Now it springs up; do you not perceive it? I am making a way in the desert and streams in the wasteland." *Isaiah 43:18–19*

Even youths grow tired and weary, and young men stumble and fall; but those who hope in the Lord will renew their strength. They will soar on wings like eagles; they will run and not grow weary, they will walk and not be faint. *Isaiah 40:30–31*

And God is able to make all grace abound to you, so that in all things at all times having all that you need, you will abound to every good work.
2 Corinthians 9:8

Ask and it will be given to you; seek and you will find; knock and the door will be opened to you. *Matthew 7:7*

And we know that in all things God works for the good of those who love him, who have been called according to his purpose. *Romans 8:28*

And God is able to make all grace abound to you, so that in all things at all times, having all that you need, you will abound in every good work.
2 Corinthians 9:8

"Be still, and know that I am God; I will be exalted among the nations, I will be exalted in the earth." *Psalm 46:10*

PRAYER

Have group members answer the question,

"How can we help you in prayer this week?"

The leader will close the group in prayer, remembering the concerns each person shared. If you would like to pray for other group members during the week, write down the prayer requests so you can remember them.

REMINDER

If you know of someone who would benefit from this course, now is the time to invite them. It would be quite easy for a new person to join your group next session.

NOTES:

[1]Jerry Gerber, Janet Wolff, Walter Klones and Gene Brown, *Lifetrends: The Future of Baby Boomers and Other Aging Americans* (New York: MacMillan, 1989), p. 22.

A New Freedom

LIFE STORIES	BIBLE STUDY

PURPOSE

To go deeper into the subject of "A New Freedom" and to share your own experience through a Bible Story about this issue.

AGENDA

 Gathering   **Study**   **Caring**

OPEN

GATHERING / 15 Minutes / All Together

Leader: Welcome any newcomers and explain the purpose of the group, the "ground rules" that you have agreed upon and the three-part agenda for the meetings. Explain that this session is the second of the two on the issue of "A New Freedom."

The purpose of the Gathering time is to break the ice. Call time after 15 minutes and move on.

Ice-Breaker: Me, As a Child. Go around on question #1, letting everyone share their answer, and then do the same with question #2.

1. Look through the following comic strip characters and pick one that best describes how you saw yourself when you were 13. Go around the group, sharing which you chose:
    ☐ Lucy—because I thought I was always right
    ☐ Charlie Brown—because nothing I did seemed to work
    ☐ Peppermint Patty—a real tomboy
    ☐ Linus—full of hang-ups and insecurities
    ☐ Calvin ("Calvin and Hobbes")—full of ideas and full of mischief
    ☐ Garfield—I wasn't overweight, I was "under-tall"!
    ☐ Cathy—obsessed with my failures with the opposite sex
    ☐ Opus ("Bloom County")—confused about what it meant to be male
    ☐ other _____

2. On the continuum below mark to what degree you were, as a child, "Mother's (or Daddy's) little helper" or "the family terror":

1	2	3	4	5
"Little helper"				**"Family terror"**

STUDY / 30 Minutes / Groups of 4

Leader: If you have more than 7 in your group, we recommend that you subdivide into groups of 4 for this Study, so that you can finish the Study in 30 minutes and everyone can participate.

INTRODUCTION

The Downside of Freedom. Sometimes we talk as if people always greet more freedom with open arms, but such is not the case. When God freed the nation of Israel from captivity in Egypt, the people soon found that freedom meant hard work, and that they lost much that was familiar and secure when they become free. Perhaps in their story we can better understand some of our own.

Have someone in your group read out loud the following Scripture. Then go around on the first question and let everyone speak up. Then, go around again on the next question, etc. Be sure to save the last 15–45 minutes for the Caring time.

16 *The whole Israelite community set out from Elim and came to the Desert of Sin, which is between Elim and Sinai, on the fifteenth day of the second month after they had come out of Egypt. ²In the desert the whole community grumbled against Moses and Aaron. ³The Israelites said to them, "If only we had died by the Lord's hand in Egypt! There we sat around pots of meat and ate all the food we wanted, but you have brought us out into this desert to starve this entire assembly to death."*

⁴Then the Lord said to Moses, "I will rain down bread from heaven for you. The people are to go out each day and gather enough for that day. In this way I will test them and see whether they will follow my instructions. ⁵On the sixth day they are to prepare what they bring in, and that is to be twice as much as they gather on the other days."

⁶So Moses and Aaron said to all the Israelites, "In the evening you will know that it was the Lord who brought you out of Egypt, ⁷and in the morning you will see the glory of the Lord, because he has heard your grumbling against him. Who are we, that you should grumble against us?" ⁸Moses also said, "You will know that it was the Lord when he gives you meat to eat in the evening and all the bread you want in the morning, because he has heard your grumbling against him. Who are we? You are not grumbling against us, but against the Lord."

Exodus 16:1–8

1. How would you describe the attitude of the Israelites in this passage?
   - ❏ About what mine is when supper's late!
   - ❏ "Better slavery with a full belly than freedom with empty cupboards."
   - ❏ "Oh, for those Good Ol' Days!"
   - ❏ "It's all God's fault!"
   - ❏ "Poor me! Why doesn't someone take care of me?!"
   - ❏ other _____

23

2. If you had been God, how would you have responded to the Israelites?
   - ❏ I'd have sent them back to Egypt—who needs the grief?
   - ❏ I'd have ordered out pizza!
   - ❏ I'd have cried and told them I was doing the best I could!
   - ❏ I'd have squashed them like so many bugs!
   - ❏ I would have shown them my power with a miracle, like he did.
   - ❏ I would have given them a reason to hope.

3. The Israelites looked back to Egypt and thought of how they missed all the good food. When you look back at your child-rearing years, what is it that you miss the most?
   - ❏ the joy and innocence of the children when they were young
   - ❏ their companionship
   - ❏ the sense of purpose which came from raising them
   - ❏ their help around the house
   - ❏ other _____

4. Finish this sentence: "The best time I remember us having together as a family when the children were young was when ..."

5. The Israelites in this story were only remembering the food, and forgetting the hard labor to which they were subjected as slaves. Which part of the "down-side" of parenting are you most glad to have behind you?
   - ❏ the fights with teenagers
   - ❏ the constant worrying about them
   - ❏ the financial demands
   - ❏ being tied down by children's schedules and kept from leaving when we want
   - ❏ having to clean up after them
   - ❏ other _____

6. As you look to your own future, what does the promise "I will rain down bread from heaven for you" mean for you?
   - ❏ The local bakery will explode.
   - ❏ God will provide what we need.
   - ❏ The God who has blessed us in the past will continue to bless us in the future.
   - ❏ This will be a time in life where we will have more than we need.

7. The Israelites grumbled because they had a hard time trusting God's provision. What do you need to do to better trust God's provision in the midst of this life change?

☐ I prefer to take care of myself, thank you!

☐ I need to stop trying to go back to the way things were.

☐ I need to learn more of God's will and direction for my life.

☐ I need to open my eyes to the "bread from heaven"—the resources God freely gives.

☐ I need to remember how God has always provided in the past.

☐ other_____

CARING / 15–45 Minutes / All Together

Leader: Regather all the groups for the Caring time. Start off with sharing. Then, if you feel comfortable, move into a time of prayer.

SHARING

Pick a weather forecast that best describes this past week in your life. Finish this sentence: "The weather in my life this past week has been ..."

☐ blue sky, bright sunshine, not a cloud in sight.

☐ partly cloudy today, 30 percent chance of rain.

☐ severe weather should continue unabated.

☐ possibility of frost again tonight, but after that, slow improvement.

☐ not much relief in sight from the heat.

☐ wind chill of minus 15.

☐ other_____

PRAYER

If there are no more than 12 in your group, stand in a circle and hold hands. Take turns going around the circle completing the following sentence:

"God, I want to thank you for ..."

Complete the sentence with what you are thankful for at the moment. If you would like to say your prayer in silence, say the word "Amen" when you have finished your prayer so the next person will know it is their turn.

A New Family Role

| LIFE STORIES | BIBLE STUDY |

PURPOSE

To introduce the subject of "A New Family Role" and to share your own life stories.

AGENDA

 Gathering Study Caring

OPEN

GATHERING / 15 Minutes / All Together

Leader: Welcome any newcomers and explain the purpose of the group, the "ground rules" and the three-part agenda of the meeting. Also, explain that this session is the first of two sessions on the subject of "A New Family Role." For more background about this topic, refer back to the Preface on page 7, paragraph 2.

Start off by reading the Introduction to the group or ask for a volunteer to read it. Then, use the Ice-Breaker to start the meeting. Remember to stick to the time limits in the 3-part agenda.

INTRODUCTION

When our last child leaves, it is almost certain that our family role will change. But in what *way* that role will change is subject to many variations. The best-case scenario is that we will change from a parent-child relationship with our children to more of a relationship of intimacy between adults. Certainly even in this there will be remnants of the old parent-child relationship around, but the basic relationship will gain a new quality. Alice Rossi, a fellow at the John D. and Catherine T. MacArthur Foundation's Research Network on Successful Midlife Development, notes that "intimacy with children, which bottoms out from ages fifteen to nineteen, climbs steeply through the [children's] twenties and thirties." She goes on to add, "One of the things to look forward to in midlife is the continuity and shared interests that will come as your children in turn become parents."[1]

However, while this new sense of intimacy often develops, there are also some roles which we find ourselves in that require new skills, and sometimes more work than we thought we had bargained for. These include grandparenting, caring for elderly parents, and helping with adult children in crisis. Grandparenting can involve anything from occasionally helping with grandchildren, a task most grandparents relish, to taking on a major parenting role for our grandchildren because our adult children cannot or will not perform it. Caring for our own elderly parents can be emotionally, and sometimes financially, draining. It becomes particularly difficult when parents become senile or unable to care for their own personal bodily needs. Similarly, helping our adult children in crisis can mean anything from an occasional loan to taking our adult children back into the home for a period of time. In all of these cases we need to be prepared to think through just how active we want to be in the helping process.

We will have two sessions on the issue of "A New Family Role," and this is the first. In this session, the emphasis will be on sharing your own story. If you wish to spend another session on this topic and go deeper into this issue, you can choose to move to Track 2 for the next session ... or you stay in Track 1 and go on to the next issue. To get started, use the Ice-Breaker below.

Ice-Breaker: Myself as an Appliance. Go around on question 1 and let everyone share. Then go around again on question 2.

1. If you could compare the role you have taken in your family down through time to a household appliance, what appliance would it be?
    - ❑ the vacuum cleaner—I pick up after everyone.
    - ❑ the washing machine agitator—When things get too calm I stir things up!
    - ❑ the heater—When people come in from the cold world I warm them up!
    - ❑ the television—I'm the entertainer.
    - ❑ the smoke alarm—I keep the others alert to dangers.
    - ❑ the thermostat—I keep things comfortable.
    - ❑ the refrigerator—I provide all of the good stuff people seem to want.
    - ❑ the electric screwdriver—I fix things and keep them running.

2. How happy are you with this role right now?

STUDY / 30 Minutes / Groups of 4

Leader: Remember, the Study in the first session on each issue (Track 1) is based on Life Stories. If there are 7 or more in your group, quickly subdivide into groups of 4 so that everyone can participate, and you can finish the Study in 30 minutes. Then, call the entire group back together at the close.

Life Stories. Have someone read out loud the stories of the two people on the next page. Then, use the questions to share some of your own experience.

Ralph

Only two years after the youngest child of Ralph and his wife Carol moved out of the house, their second youngest moved back in. The second youngest, Linda, had just been divorced and she had no marketable job skills. She had two little boys, 5 and 6 years old. Both were upset that their dad wasn't around. Ralph felt it was his role to "fill in" for the missing father image. He enjoyed doing this, but it wore him down. In addition, the boys still missed their father and were subject to temper fits. It seemed to Ralph that there was no place he could go for some peace and quiet.

Rhonda

The same year Rhonda's only son went away to college, her father died of a heart attack, leaving her mother alone. Rhonda's mother had always depended heavily on her husband, and hadn't even learned how to drive. Rhonda's brother and sister both lived out of town, and so Rhonda was the only one who could effectively help. At first this consisted mostly of running errands for her and taking her to the various places she needed to go. But she started to have more and more problems with her health that necessitated that either her mother stay with Rhonda or Rhonda stay with her mother. Rhonda's husband, Greg, went along with all of this at first, but soon the needs of Rhonda's mother kept them from being able to take any of the out-of-town trips they had been wanting to take together. Greg was beginning to think that Rhonda's mother was acting more dependent than she really needed to be, and he resented the impositions more and more.

DISCUSS

Questions:

1. Which of the family issues these two people were dealing with have you met yourself?
   - ☐ having an adult child move in
   - ☐ helping an adult child going through divorce
   - ☐ feeling I had to be a substitute parent to grandchildren
   - ☐ feeling my peace and quiet invaded by the needs of grandchildren
   - ☐ needing to care for one parent after the other died
   - ☐ having to care for a sick parent
   - ☐ feeling imposed upon by an elderly parent

2. Alice Rossi is quoted in the Introduction as saying that intimacy with children normally bottoms out in the late teens and then climbs through the 20s and 30s. How does that compare to your experience? On a scale of 1 to 10 rate the closeness you felt to your oldest child (or whichever child you would chose to report on) in each of the following age ranges:

PRESCHOOL

1	2	3	4	5	6	7	8	9	10

Barely speaking   **Best pals**

GRADE SCHOOL

1	2	3	4	5	6	7	8	9	10

Barely speaking   **Best pals**

JUNIOR HIGH

1	2	3	4	5	6	7	8	9	10

Barely speaking   **Best pals**

HIGH SCHOOL

1	2	3	4	5	6	7	8	9	10

Barely speaking   **Best pals**

NOW

1	2	3	4	5	6	7	8	9	10

Barely speaking   **Best pals**

3. Which of the following options are unacceptable to you when it comes to caring for the needs of adult children and their families? (Mark as many as apply.)
    - ❏ giving them a loan
    - ❏ helping them with regular financial support
    - ❏ taking them back into the home for a few months
    - ❏ taking them back into our home long term
    - ❏ doing occasional baby sitting
    - ❏ providing regular childcare
    - ❏ taking grandchildren into our home as our own

4. Which of the following options are unacceptable to you when it comes to caring for the needs of your own aging parents?
   - ❏ helping them with household and yard chores
   - ❏ giving them regular financial support
   - ❏ handling their finances and personal business
   - ❏ providing transportation for them
   - ❏ nursing one or both of them when sick
   - ❏ taking them into our home
   - ❏ putting one or both into a nursing home

5. What is the most difficult decision you have had to make to this point when it comes to caring either for adult children or aging parents?

6. What help would you like from this group when it comes to determining what your new family role should be?
   - ❏ someone to just commiserate with
   - ❏ someone else who is going through it to share ideas with
   - ❏ someone to understand when my parents/adult children are trying to make me feel guilty
   - ❏ someone to pray with over these issues
   - ❏ other _____

CARING / 15–45 Minutes / All Together

Leader: Bring all the groups back together for the Caring time. Start off the sharing by asking for prayer requests. Then, if you are comfortable, ask people to take these requests to God in a time of prayer.

SHARING

Have someone in your group read Philippians 4:12–13,

I know what it is to be in need, and I know what it is to have plenty. I have learned the secret of being content in any and every situation, whether well fed or hungry, whether living in plenty or in want. I can do everything through him who gives me strength.

As you reflect on this Scripture passage, in what area or concern in your life do you have trouble accepting or feeling God's contentment?

PRAYER

Remembering what people shared, close in prayer, thanking God for each other and what you are experiencing as a group.

NOTES:

[1]Quoted in Jim Smoke, *Facing 50: A View From the Mountaintop* (Nashville: Thomas Nelson, 1994), p. 168.

A New Family Role

LIFE STORIES	BIBLE STUDY

PURPOSE

To go deeper into the subject of "A New Family Role" and to relate your experience to a story in the Bible.

AGENDA

 Gathering   Study   Caring

OPEN

GATHERING / 15 Minutes / All Together

Leader: Welcome any newcomers and explain the purpose of the group, the "ground rules" and the three-part agenda of the meetings. Explain that this session is the second of two on the subject of "A New Family Role."

The purpose of the Gathering time is to break the ice. Call time after 15 minutes and move on.

Ice-Breaker: Circus Acts. Go around and let each person answer one of the questions below, or both.

1. If you were to compare how you are handling your life right now to a circus act, which act would it be?
    ❑ a trapeze artist—flying high, but hoping not to fall
    ❑ a lion tamer—keeping the frightening things at bay
    ❑ a clown—laughing even when I fall on my face
    ❑ a clown—laughing on the outside, but crying on the inside
    ❑ a juggler—keeping a lot of things going
    ❑ the strong man—taking a lot on my shoulders
    ❑ the "freak show"—feeling out-of-place and stared at by others
    ❑ the magician—the world seems at my command
    ❑ other _____

2. If you were a magician, what would you most like to have magically disappear?
    ❑ all my temptations   ❑ my boss
    ❑ my bills   ❑ my responsibilities this week
    ❑ my bad memories   ❑ my adult children from my house
    ❑ my ex-spouse   ❑ my ex-spouse's spouse
    ❑ a bodily ailment   ❑ other_____

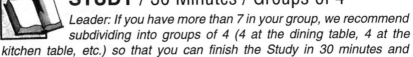

STUDY / 30 Minutes / Groups of 4

Leader: If you have more than 7 in your group, we recommend subdividing into groups of 4 (4 at the dining table, 4 at the kitchen table, etc.) so that you can finish the Study in 30 minutes and everyone can participate.

INTRODUCTION

Jesus' New Family Role. Jesus never married, and so he never had children and experienced "the empty nest." But he did come to a point in his life where he took on a new family role, and he did have to deal with a mother who was not too sure she wanted him to leave the safety of "the family nest." Most biblical scholars believe that Jesus' earthly father died shortly after Jesus was 12 years old, for that is the last time we hear of his father. Therefore, as the eldest son, he probably had to take on the role of the "man of the house" for many years. However, when he was 30 he left the home to begin his three-year ministry of teaching and healing. In that ministry he met much stress, opposition and danger. It is probably in reaction to that stress, opposition and danger that his mother came to "rescue" him in the following little story.

Have someone in your group read the story out loud. Then, go around on the first question and let everyone speak up. Then, go around again on the next question, etc. Remember, there are no right or wrong answers, so you don't have to feel intimidated by one who is more familiar with the Bible. Be sure to save the last 15–45 minutes for the Caring time.

²⁰Then Jesus entered a house, and again a crowd gathered, so that he and his disciples were not even able to eat. ²¹When his family heard about this, they went to take charge of him, for they said, "He is out of his mind"...

³¹Then Jesus' mother and brothers arrived. Standing outside, they sent someone in to call him. ³²A crowd was sitting around him, and they told him, "Your mother and brothers are outside looking for you."

³³"Who are my mother and brothers?" he asked.

³⁴Then he looked at those seated in a circle around him and said, "Here are my mother and my brothers! ³⁵Whoever does God's will is my brother and sister and mother."

Mark 3:20–21,31–35

1. When Jesus' mother and brothers came to "rescue" him, what do you think was Jesus' predominant feeling?
   - ❑ embarrassed over her doing this in front of his followers
   - ❑ angry that she was treating him like a kid
   - ❑ angry that she didn't understand
   - ❑ thankful she cared
   - ❑ nostalgic—maybe he wanted to go back home!

2. When as an adult has your mother or father done something so embarrassing to you that you thought of disowning them?

3. When should a parent try to rescue an adult child from difficult times, and when should a parent not do so?

4. How would you describe the family role that Jesus was taking here?
   ❐ a rebellious son
   ❐ a role reversal—the son was teaching the parent
   ❐ a brother in a new, wider family
   ❐ other _____

5. What group in your life has been most like family to you, as the disciples were to Jesus?

6. What makes a person feel most like a "mother, sister or brother" to you?
   ❐ when they listen to me
   ❐ when they spend a lot of time with me
   ❐ when they share common experiences with me
   ❐ when they are there for me when I need them
   ❐ when they are honest and open with me
   ❐ when they stick with me even after we have gotten angry with each other
   ❐ other _____

7. When have you tried to "rescue" your own adult child from a stressful or difficult time. Looking back, do you think your actions were appropriate or interfering?

8. What has happened in this group that has helped you feel more like "mothers, brothers and sisters" to each other?

CARING / 15–45 Minutes / All Together

Leader: Regather the entire group for the Caring time. The purpose of the Caring time in this session is to spend time in caring support for each other through sharing prayer requests and prayer.

SHARING

Take time to share any personal prayer requests by answering the question:

"How can we help you in prayer this week?"

Think especially of any situations where you often tend to get down on yourself.

PRAYER

Close with a time of prayer, remembering the requests that have been shared. If you would like to pray in silence, say the word "Amen" when you have finished your prayer, so the next person will know when to start.

<table>
<tr><td>

</td><td colspan="2">

A New Purpose
</td></tr>
<tr><td></td><td>**LIFE STORIES**</td><td>**BIBLE STUDY**</td></tr>
</table>

PURPOSE To introduce the subject of "A New Purpose" and to support one another.

AGENDA  Gathering   Study   Caring

OPEN

GATHERING / 15 Minutes / All Together

Leader: Welcome the newcomers and explain the purpose and procedures of the group. Explain that this session is the first of two sessions on "A New Purpose."

Start off by reading the Introduction to the group or ask for a volunteer to read it. Then, use the Ice-Breaker to start the meeting. Remember to keep to the 3-part agenda.

INTRODUCTION Besides being a time of changing family roles, the time of the empty nest is also a time of flux in relation to one's sense of purpose. For most men, as well as more and more women, sense of purpose is closely tied to paid work. This creates problems for two reasons. One is that most men face retirement at 65 to 70. Where does sense of purpose come from then? In addition, many men in their 50s lose the job that had been their profession for the earlier part of their life. The Bureau of Labor Statistics shows that from October 1991 to October 1992 the unemployment rate in those aged 55 and older was seven times that of those aged 16–54. The middle management group, which consists primarily of people in their 50s, has been particularly hard hit.[1] Again, losing what has been our profession generally calls our sense of life purpose into question.

Most women, on the other hand, have traditionally gotten their sense of purpose from their role as mother. When children leave home, what happens to that sense of purpose? Counselor Jim Smoke finds that women react to this change by taking on one of four identities: (1) **Nurturers,** where their identities are now tied to the vocation of their husband, the careers of their older children, and the care and nurturing of their grandchildren; (2) **Discoverers,** who rework the structure of their lives by pursuing a career or vocation on a full-time basis; (3) **Achievers,** who really don't need to change as much as they have worked diligently at a career for most of their lives while also raising a family; and (4) **Displaced homemakers**, who have been forced into the job market due to a divorce or the illness or death of a husband. Smoke finds that "nurturers" seem to comprise the smallest portion of women in their 50s, while the largest group seems to be the "discoverers."[2] For those in this latter category, Cynthia Coad has written a handbook to help women with this transition called, *Your Full Future: After the Empty Nest*. She writes in that book, "The first one-half of the female's life has been occupied in serving others. It was a path she chose, and one she accomplished well. In many cases this meant that her own personal career goals were not fully developed. A time comes, however, when the woman looks for her full future in the form of a career. The second one-half of her life offers her that opportunity."[3] And so, whether one is male or female, the time of the empty nest can be a time when we look to a new life purpose.

This is the first of two sessions on "A New Purpose." To get started, use the Ice-Breaker.

Ice-Breaker: Just My Style. Go around on question #1, letting everyone share their answer, and then do the same with question #2, etc. If your time is limited, you may want to choose two of the three questions.

1. When it comes to fashion, I'm the kind of person who ...
   - ❑ breaks out in hives if I have to wear a suit or dress.
   - ❑ thinks "formal dress" means my jeans without the holes in them.
   - ❑ brags about "second hand" consignment bargains.
   - ❑ wears whatever my spouse buys me.
   - ❑ purposely aspires to the "worst-dressed" list.
   - ❑ wears what I like, whether it's in fashion or not.
   - ❑ insists on designer labels—even on my underwear!
   - ❑ keeps with the fashion, as best as I can afford.
   - ❑ tries to set fashion trends myself.

2. When it comes to movies, my style is more like ...
   - ❑ old time romances, like Humphrey Bogart and Lauren Bacall.
   - ❑ old time comedies, like with Bob Hope or Jerry Lewis.
   - ❑ action pictures with Stephen Segal or Arnold Schwarzneggar.
   - ❑ modern comedies like Robin Williams or Whoopi Goldberg.
   - ❑ modern romances, with people like Tom Cruise or Meg Ryan.
   - ❑ animated family pictures, like "The Lion King."
   - ❑ mysteries or thrillers, like "The Client."
   - ❑ touching personal stories like "Forrest Gump" or "Little Women."

3. And then when you talk about eating out, my style is more like ...
   - ❑ McDonald's or Burger King.
   - ❑ anywhere with good pizza.
   - ❑ a good steak house.
   - ❑ a fine seafood restaurant by the ocean.
   - ❑ Mexican food that brings the steam out my ears.
   - ❑ a restaurant with exotic cuisine at the top of a skyscraper.
   - ❑ a health food restaurant with creative recipes.

STUDY / 30 Minutes / Groups of 4

Leader: If there are more than 7 in your group, quickly sub-divide into groups of 4 so that everyone can participate, and you can finish the Study in 30 minutes. Then, call all of the groups back together for the Caring time.

Life Stories. Have someone read aloud the stories of the two people below. Then, use the questions to share some of your own experience.

Kevin

Not long after his youngest daughter got married Kevin lost his job. He had been working at a large computer firm in California when there was a big lay-off. Kevin had thought he would be protected by his seniority, but it didn't work that way. At 52 he found that not many firms were interested in hiring him. After using up much of his savings he took a job selling used cars. Even worse than the economic trouble this brought was a more personal struggle—he felt he was without worth. No one wanted him. He had spent his life developing certain skills, which no one now seemed to be willing to pay for. He felt like he had been cast aside onto a garbage heap.

Ellen

Over 30 years ago Ellen had dropped out of college to marry the man of her dreams. Now after having and raising three children with that man, she is going back. When her youngest son went away to college she had a sudden urge to pack her bags and go with him. At first she thought it was because she wanted to be with him, but then she realized it was because she wanted to do what he was *doing*. It was a year later when she decided it was her turn. She opted for a college in the city where she lived, where she decided to get a degree in business administration. She thought at first that she would feel out of place with all of the younger people, but when she entered her first class, she found a number of women just like her.

DISCUSS | **Questions:**

1. What was the first job you had outside of the home? What is your most vivid memory of that experience?

2. If you could go back to college right now, as Ellen did, and money was no object, what subject would you choose to study?

3. Which of the experiences the two people in our case studies had have you also experienced?
    ❑ losing a job after many years with a company, like Kevin
    ❑ being forced to take a job I didn't like because of my age, like Kevin
    ❑ feeling like I had been cast aside on the garbage heap professionally, like Kevin
    ❑ having given up college for marriage, like Ellen
    ❑ going back to college after years of raising children, like Ellen

4. It is said that men get most of their life meaning from work, and women from their family or relational roles. Is that true in your case? Mark the scale below:

mostly relational	a little of both	mostly professional

5. Women, which of Jim Smoke's four categories of how women respond to the "empty nest" sounds most like you?
    ❑ nurturer—still caring for others, like my grandkids!
    ❑ discoverer—exploring my skills in a paid vocation
    ❑ achiever—balancing home and work all along
    ❑ displaced homemaker—working because I have to

6. Men, how would you describe the role your profession plays in your life right now?
    ❑ It's a pay check.
    ❑ I'm just waiting for the chance to retire!
    ❑ What profession?—I'm out of work!
    ❑ I'm looking for something more satisfying.
    ❑ It's my life!—but what happens when I retire?
    ❑ It's my life and I'm not going to retire!

7. As you look to your future, what do you need to do to develop a new sense of purpose in your life?
    ❑ look into a new profession
    ❑ learn to find purpose in my new family roles
    ❑ find purpose by developing my spiritual life
    ❑ find a meaningful way of contributing to others through volunteer work
    ❑ find meaning in every moment of life, by experiencing it fully
    ❑ continue to find purpose in my paid profession until I die

CARING / 15–45 Minutes / All Together

Leader: To close this session, call the groups back together to join in the sharing and prayer.

SHARING

Have one member of the group read John 14:12–13a:

"I tell you the truth, anyone who has faith in me will do what I have been doing. He will do even greater things than these, because I am going to the Father. And I will do whatever you ask in my name ..."

Share, which of the following kinds of strengths would you ask for in Jesus' name, that you might do the great things that God still has planned for you to do?

       ❐ strength to try new things
       ❐ strength to believe in the talents God has given me
       ❐ strength to face change boldly
       ❐ strength to not hold on to the past
       ❐ strength to reach out to others to work with me
       ❐ strength to focus on serving God and others
       ❐ other _____

PRAYER

Remembering what people shared, close in prayer. Again, remember that if you would like to pray in silence, say the word "Amen" when you have finished your prayer, so the next person will know when to start.

NOTES:

[1] Jim Smoke, *Facing 50: A View From the Mountaintop* (Nashville: Thomas Nelson, 1994), p. 126.
[2] Ibid., p. 52.
[3] Cynthia Coad, *Your Full Future: After the Empty Nest* (Muncie, Ind.; Accelerated Development Inc., 1989), p. 3.

A New Purpose

| LIFE STORIES | BIBLE STUDY |

PURPOSE

To go deeper into the issue of "A New Purpose" and to identify with a story in Scripture related to this topic.

AGENDA

 Gathering Study Caring

OPEN

 GATHERING / 15 Minutes / All Together

Leader: Welcome newcomers and explain the purpose and the procedures of the group. Explain that this session is the second of two sessions on "A New Purpose."

The purpose of the Gathering time is to break the ice. Call time after 15 minutes and move on.

Ice-Breaker: Our "Un-Calling." To recognize our calling or purpose at this stage of life, perhaps it might help to first eliminate some callings we would like to avoid. We can call this our "un-calling!"

Look over the list below and decide which you would least like to do, and share it with your group:

- ❏ crowd control officer at a rock concert
- ❏ organizer of paperwork for Congress
- ❏ script writer for Barney and Baby Bop
- ❏ manager of public relations for Madonna
- ❏ bodyguard for Rush Limbaugh on a speaking tour of feminist groups
- ❏ middle high principal
- ❏ nurses aide at a home for retired Sumo wrestlers with Alzheimers
- ❏ official physician for the National Association of Hypochondriacs

STUDY / 30 Minutes / Groups of 4

Leader: If you have more than 7 in your group, we recommend subdividing into groups of 4 (4 at the dining table, 4 at the kitchen table, etc.) so that you can finish the Study in 30 minutes and everyone can participate.

INTRODUCTION

Taking on Too Little. For centuries the people of Israel saw as their purpose bringing their own nation back to God. Time and again they failed at that purpose, as their people strayed after other gods. But what does God then do? Does he decide to be content with less than what he originally asked? No! He tells them that the task that they have been struggling with is too small! He now wants them to know that the full task to which they are called is to be "a light to the nations"—to help other people come to God as well. As you read about how God helped Israel redefine their purpose, see what it says to you about the purpose to which God calls you.

Have someone in your group read the passage out loud. Then go around on the first question and let everyone speak up. Then go around again on the next question, etc. Be sure to save the last 15–45 minutes for the Caring time.

49
*Listen to me, you islands;
 hear this, you distant nations:
before I was born the Lord called me;
 from my birth he has made mention of my name.
²He made my mouth like a sharpened sword,
 in the shadow of his hand he hid me;
he made me into a polished arrow
 and concealed me in his quiver.
³He said to me, "You are my servant,
 Israel, in whom I will display my splendor."
⁴But I said, "I have labored to no purpose;
 I have spent my strength in vain and for nothing.
Yet what is due me is in the Lord's hand,
 and my reward is with my God."
⁵And now the Lord says—
 he who formed me in the womb to be his servant
to bring Jacob back to him and gather Israel to himself,
for I am honored in the eyes of the Lord
 and my God has been my strength —
⁶he says:
"It is too small a thing for you to be my servant
to restore the tribes of Jacob
and bring back those of Israel I have kept.
I will also make you a light for the Gentiles,
 that you may bring my salvation to the ends of the earth."*

Isaiah 49:1–6

1. If you were part of the nation of Israel at this time, how would you have felt when God said that the task you had been struggling with for generations was "too small a thing"?
    - ❏ "Oh yeah? You try it!"
    - ❏ "I think I'll just give up and go fishing!"
    - ❏ "You're expecting too much of us!"
    - ❏ "Well, if God thinks we can do it, maybe ..."
    - ❏ "Great! I love a challenge!"

2. Why do you think God "expanded their job description" when the nation was failing?
    - ❏ to punish them
    - ❏ He figured they weren't challenged enough and needed to be in "the enriched program."
    - ❏ to show them how far behind they were
    - ❏ to show them God was concerned about other nations too

3. Isaiah felt he was "born to preach;" others have felt they were "born to be wild." Which of the following is more like what you were "born to do"?
    - ❏ Born to shop!
    - ❏ Born to boogie!
    - ❏ Born to shoot hoops!
    - ❏ Born to lead!
    - ❏ Born to _____!
    - ❏ Born to fish!
    - ❏ I'll still go with "born to be wild"!
    - ❏ Born to sip margaritas and lie in the sun!

4. When in your life have you felt, like Israel, "I have labored to no purpose?"
    - ❏ when I was in school learning stuff I considered useless
    - ❏ when one of our children rebelled against us
    - ❏ when I was fired or laid off
    - ❏ when I couldn't get a job coming out of college
    - ❏ when I planned a project which no one seemed to appreciate
    - ❏ when my boss took credit for my work
    - ❏ every time I cleaned and someone messed it up!

5. If God were to point to something you have been focusing on in your life, and call it "too small a thing" to spend all your life on, what do you suspect it might be?
    - ❏ just making money
    - ❏ only looking after myself
    - ❏ watching television
    - ❏ other _____
    - ❏ just doing enough to get by at work
    - ❏ providing only for my own family and ignoring needs of others

6. What new, larger purpose do you think God might be calling you to right now?

CARING / 15–45 Minutes / All Together

Leader: Spend some time evaluating the experience in the group up to this point. Then, close with prayer.

EVALUATION

This is the midpoint in this course. Use this opportunity to take your pulse and make any necessary mid-course corrections. Start off with the exercises below. Then, close in prayer.

How would you describe your small group? Choose one of the images below which best describes your small group, then go around your group and tell them why you chose the one you did.

AN ORCHARD: Whenever I'm in this group I feel like a fragrant, healthy apple tree because of all the growing I've done and all the fruit I've been able to share.

BIRD NEST: I know how a baby bird feels because being a part of this group makes me feel nurtured and protected.

OASIS: While the rest of the world can be so harsh and unforgiving, this group is a refreshing stop on the journey of life.

THE 12 MUSKETEERS: It's "All for one and one for all" with this group. I always feel like I belong and I'm part of a great team.

A LITTER OF PUPPIES: You are a fun, friendly and enthusiastic bundle of joy. I feel younger every time we are together.

M*A*S*H* UNIT: This group is like a field hospital. I came in wounded and now I feel so much better and I have a bunch of friends to boot!

TEEPEE: We couldn't stand tall and provide warmth and shelter if we didn't lean on each other.

THE BRADY BUNCH: I feel like I'm part of one big happy family. We're not perfect, but we love and accept each other.

THINK TANK: This group must be full of geniuses! We seem to be able to understand every issue and work out every problem with creativity and discernment.

PRAYER

Close with a time of prayer. If you would like to pray in silence, say the word "Amen," when you have finished your prayer, so that the next person will know when to start.

A New Marriage Partnership

LIFE STORIES	BIBLE STUDY

PURPOSE

To introduce the issue of "A New Marriage Partnership" and continue to support each other.

AGENDA

 Gathering   Study   Caring

OPEN

 GATHERING / 15 Minutes / All Together

Leader: Welcome newcomers and explain the purpose and procedures in this group. Explain that this session is the first session on "A New Marriage Partnership."

Start off by reading the Introduction to the group or ask for a volunteer to read it. Then, use the Ice-Breaker to start the meeting. Remember to keep to the 3-part agenda.

INTRODUCTION

Growing and changing are the central indications that something is living, and so if our marriage is truly alive it must change and grow. Especially is this true when the last child leaves the home. When children are in the home much activity centers around them. They provide a common focus for parents who share in the task of raising them. But when they are gone, what will then be the common focus that the couple has to hold them together? Many couples at this stage discover that the children were the *only* thing they had in common. This discovery generally means a time of strain for the marriage, unless they explore and discover some common interests. What is more, since the empty nest period has other big life changes, like a woman's new professional explorations, or a man's retirement, unless a couple learns to adapt to those changes, the marital strain will be even more severe. Those marriages which survive and even thrive in this period are those where both persons are willing to change and to not hold on to the past relationship, but look forward to a new, different and exciting one.

We will have two sessions on the issue of developing a new marriage partnership, and this is the first. In this session, the emphasis will be on sharing your own story. If you wish to spend another session on this topic and go deeper into this issue, you can choose to move to Track 2 for the next session ... or you can stay in Track 1 and go on to the next issue.

This is the first of two sessions on "A New Marriage Partnership." Use the Ice-Breaker to get started.

Ice-Breaker: My Romantic Scenario. Describe your perfect romantic day by finishing the sentences below. In this fantasy, money is no object, so let your imagination run wild! Instead of taking one question at a time, have each person share their whole scenario before going on to the next person.

1. "For my perfect romantic day we would travel by Lear jet to ..."
    - ❏ Paris.
    - ❏ Rome.
    - ❏ San Francisco.
    - ❏ Maui.
    - ❏ the outback of Australia.
    - ❏ Puerto Vallarta.
    - ❏ our own little island.
    - ❏ Venice.
    - ❏ New York.
    - ❏ Honolulu.
    - ❏ Switzerland.
    - ❏ Vail.
    - ❏ other _____

2. "We would spend the day ...
    - ❏ playing on a beach.
    - ❏ shopping & exploring.
    - ❏ meeting new people.
    - ❏ other _____
    - ❏ talking and walking hand in hand.
    - ❏ in recreational pursuits, like skiing.
    - ❏ sipping cold drinks under a parasol.

3. At dinner I would have (singer's name) flown in to sing (a favorite song) just for us.

4. We would top off the evening by ...
    - ❏ dancing all night
    - ❏ taking a walk under the stars.
    - ❏ going to a special concert
    - ❏ exploring ... between the sheets!
    - ❏ other _____

STUDY / 30 Minutes / Groups of 4

Leader: If there are more than 7 in your group, quickly sub-divide into groups of 4 so that everyone can participate, and you can finish the Study in 30 minutes. Then, call all of the groups back together for the Caring time.

Life Stories. Have someone read out loud the stories of the two people below. Then, use the questions to share some of your own experience.

Ann
In relation to how their children's leaving changed their marriage, Ann says, "It's almost as if we had gotten remarried ... When we were dating

—all those years ago—we kept looking forward to the time when we would be married. We were anxious for it to happen; we dreamed about it and shared those dreams with each other. Then the kids came along and somehow being married, being husband and wife, took second place to being Mom and Dad." Ann later told how toward the end of those "Mom and Dad" years, a new kind of anticipation started growing within her and her husband: "It happened slowly, now that I think about it. One day my husband looked up from a sports magazine and said, 'Someday I'd like to go fishing in Alaska.' I said, 'Yeah, me too. We'll do it when the kids are gone.' After that, the phrase, 'when the kids are gone,' kept popping up in our conversations. It was like when we were back in those days when we had said, 'When we're married we'll do so-and-so.' We started anticipating all the fun things we would do when the kids were out on their own."[1]

Virginia

After Virginia's youngest daughter, Kim, got married she confided to a friend, "You know, I have really been dreading this. Tom [her husband] will be retiring soon, and I have no idea what we are going to do. He already is irritable most of the time when he is home, and we hardly ever talk. The only one I have been able to really talk to has been Kim, and now she's moving 200 miles away. I'm trying to think up as many projects as I can to keep Tom busy, but I wonder how long it will last."

DISCUSS

Questions:

1. Ann's excitement about what they would do when the kids were gone reminded her of the time they were dating. What most reminds you of the time you were dating?
   - ❏ hearing certain songs on the radio
   - ❏ pictures we have around the house
   - ❏ seeing a certain look on my spouse's face sometimes that reminds me of then
   - ❏ when I see young people out dating at places we used to go
   - ❏ like with Ann—the excitement of being just a couple again

2. What advice would you give to Virginia about how to handle the change in their home situation?
   - ❏ like she says—give him a lot of projects!
   - ❏ call her daughter a lot, and let her husband fend for himself
   - ❏ plan trips together, not projects!
   - ❏ get marriage counseling
   - ❏ find things to talk about
   - ❏ other _____

49

3. When you first approached your empty nest time, were you more approaching it with excitement about the things you would do, like Ann, or with anxiety, like Virginia?

   _____

   anxiety   **a little of both**   **excitement**

4. Virginia and her husband hardly ever talked. In any given week, what are your most significant conversations about right now?
   - ❏ what's on TV
   - ❏ bills that must be paid, meetings we have to go to, etc.
   - ❏ plans for the future
   - ❏ the children and grandchildren
   - ❏ jobs that need to be done around the house
   - ❏ our jobs
   - ❏ politics and the world situation
   - ❏ God and spirituality

5. If you could talk to your spouse about anything you wanted to, what would you most like to talk to him or her about?
   - ❏ my childhood
   - ❏ my job
   - ❏ my fears about the future
   - ❏ my hopes and dreams
   - ❏ my favorite sport or hobby
   - ❏ our children and grandchildren
   - ❏ God and my spiritual needs
   - ❏ other _____

6. What most needs to happen to make your empty nest time a time of renewing your marriage relationship?
   - ❏ We need to explore mutual interests.
   - ❏ We need to let go of the past.
   - ❏ We need to pray together more.
   - ❏ We need to free up more time to talk to each other.
   - ❏ We need to find some projects we can work on together.

7. If you could choose a song right now for the *future* of your marriage, what song might you choose?
   - ❏ "I Think We're Alone Now" (Tommy James & the Shondells)
   - ❏ "You and Me Against the World" (Helen Reddy)
   - ❏ "Have I Told You Lately (That I Love You?)" (Rod Stewart)
   - ❏ "Don't Get Around Much Anymore" (Nat King Cole)
   - ❏ "Still Crazy After All These Years" (Paul Simon)
   - ❏ "Let's Stay Together" (Tina Turner)
   - ❏ "A Whole New World" (from the movie "Aladdin")

CARING / 15–45 Minutes / All Together

Leader: Regather everyone for the Caring time. Spend some time sharing, then close in prayer.

SHARING

In silence, read over the promises below. Choose one that best speaks to your situation today in a personal way, read it to the group, and tell them why you chose it.

Ask and it will be given to you; seek and you will find; knock and the door will be opened to you. For everyone who asks receives; he who seeks finds; and to him who knocks, the door will be opened.
Matthew 7:7–8

Do not be anxious about anything, but in everything, by prayer and petition, with thanksgiving, present your requests to God. And the peace of God, which transcends all understanding, will guard your hearts and your minds in Christ Jesus.
Philippians 4:6–7

Therefore, I urge you, brothers, in view of God's mercy, to offer your bodies as living sacrifices, holy and pleasing to God—this is your spiritual act of worship. Do not conform any longer to the pattern of this world, but be transformed by the renewing of your mind. Then you will be able to test and approve what God's will is—his good, pleasing and perfect will.
Romans 12:1–2

... being confident of this, that he who began a good work in you will carry it on to completion until the day of Christ Jesus.
Philippians 1:6

Call to me and I will answer you and tell you great and unsearchable things you do not know.
Jeremiah 33:3

The Lord will guide you always; he will satisfy your needs in a sun-scorched land and will strengthen your frame. You will be like a well-watered garden, like a spring whose waters never fail.
Isaiah 59:11

PRAYER

Share with the group your answer to the question,

"How can we help you in prayer this week?"

Close with a time of prayer, remembering the requests that have been shared. If you would like to pray in silence, say the word "Amen" when you have finished your prayer, so that the next person will know when to start.

NOTE:
[1] The pseudonym of "Ann" was given to a woman whose story was first reported in Jim Smoke, *Facing 50: A View From the Mountaintop* (Nashville: Thomas Nelson, 1994), p. 33.

A New Marriage Partnership

LIFE STORIES	BIBLE STUDY

PURPOSE

To go deeper into the subject of "A New Marriage Partnership" by relating your experience to a story in Scripture.

AGENDA

 Gathering Study Caring

OPEN

 **GATHERING** / 15 Minutes / All Together

Leader: Welcome newcomers and explain the purpose and procedure of the group. Explain that this session is the second of two sessions on the issue of "A New Marriage Partnership."

The purpose of the Gathering time is to break the ice. Call time after 15 minutes and move on.

Ice-Breaker: Life's Embarrassing Moments. Transitions typically have some tense or even embarrassing moments due to the uncertainty people have about how to behave or what to expect. As you look back over your life, which of the following transitions brought you the most embarrassment? Tell as much as you can remember about your experience so we can blush right along with you!

- ❏ going to junior high and having to shower in front of the other kids
- ❏ going to a junior high dance and getting up the nerve to ask someone to dance
- ❏ first time I kissed someone of the opposite sex (outside of family)
- ❏ meeting my future in-laws for the first time and saying the wrong thing
- ❏ fixing that meal when we were first married and I tried a "new recipe"!
- ❏ that time at my first job when I realized they don't teach you everything in school
- ❏ the day I realized my teenager didn't want me around in public
- ❏ meeting my teenage child's date and saying the wrong thing

STUDY / 30 Minutes / Groups of 4

Leader: If you have more than 7 in your group, we recommend subdividing into groups of 4 (4 at the dining table, 4 at the kitchen table, etc.) so that you can finish the Study in 30 minutes and everyone can participate.

INTRODUCTION

A Couple With a Mission. The following story is about a couple who apparently played quite an important role in the early history of the church. We don't know that they were "empty nesters," but what seems evident is that they were not preoccupied at this stage with the task of raising children. Rather they had a business of their own, tent making, and in addition took an active role in missionary work. As we consider their story it can help us to think about what challenges we might attempt together.

Have someone read the passage out loud. Then, go around on the first question and let everyone speak up. Then, go around on the next question, etc. Be sure to save the last 15–45 minutes for the Caring time.

18 *After this, Paul left Athens and went to Corinth. ²There he met a Jew named Aquila, a native of Pontus, who had recently come from Italy with his wife Priscilla, because Claudius had ordered all the Jews to leave Rome. Paul went to see them, ³and because he was a tentmaker as they were, he stayed and worked with them ...*

¹⁸Paul stayed on in Corinth for some time. Then he left the brothers and sailed for Syria, accompanied by Priscilla and Aquila. Before he sailed, he had his hair cut off at Cenchrea because of a vow he had taken. ¹⁹They arrived at Ephesus, where Paul had left Priscilla and Aquila. He himself went into the synagogue and reasoned with the Jews. ²⁰When they asked him to spend more time with them, he declined ...

²⁴Meanwhile a Jew named Apollos, a native of Alexandria, came to Ephesus. He was a learned man, with a thorough knowledge of the Scriptures. ²⁵He had been instructed in the way of the Lord, and he spoke with great fervor and taught about Jesus accurately, though he knew only the baptism of John. ²⁶He began to speak boldly in the synagogue. When Priscilla and Aquila heard him, they invited him to their home and explained to him the way of God more adequately.

Acts 18:1–3, 18–20, 24–26

1. Priscilla and Aquila were forced to leave their original homeland, Italy, by a government edict. Where do you consider to be your original home, and what caused you to leave from there?

2. On their life journey, Priscilla and Aquila encountered Paul and Apollos, one of whom was a teacher to them, and one of whom they taught. Who was one of your early mentors in life? Who have you in turn mentored?

53

3. Priscilla and Aquila apparently had the gift of hospitality, as they took both Paul (v. 3) and Apollos (v. 26) into their home. They also apparently had a gift of teaching (v. 26.) What would you say are the most important gifts you have (as a couple or individual)? (Mark as many as apply)

   ❏ hospitality also—People feel cared for in our home.

   ❏ teaching—People seem to respond when we share what we have learned.

   ❏ administration—One or both of us are good at getting things done.

   ❏ listening—People feel heard in our presence.

   ❏ visitation—We enjoy spending time with strangers and the sick, making them feel cared about.

   ❏ mercy—We have a heart for the oppressed, and identify with their issues.

   ❏ evangelism—We help people hear the Good News in terms they can understand.

   ❏ serving—Whether by waiting on tables, cleaning floors or fixing what needs to be fixed, we do the sometimes menial tasks that often get overlooked.

   ❏ other _____

4. In what ways did you use your gift or gifts when your children were in your home?

5. Now that your children are grown, what ways could you, like Priscilla and Aquila, use your gifts to serve God and others?

6. Back in the Preface at the beginning of this book, William H. Bergquist, Elinor Miller Greenberg and G. Alan Klaum are quoted as saying in regard to the time of the empty nest, "When couples fail to develop a new intimacy in these years, the problem is usually they no longer have any common interests ... They discover new time together in their fifties but have nothing to share in that time." In light of this, how do you think finding a ministry or service project in which to share might affect your marriage?

   ❏ disastrous!—It would take our free time and wear us out.

   ❏ mostly bad—We would focus more on the project than each other.

   ❏ mostly good—At least it would give us something to do together.

   ❏ It would be great!—A common commitment would bind us together.

   ❏ We're already doing this!

7. What would be the biggest obstacle you might face in attempting to have such a ministry or service project in common?

- ❐ disrupting our TV schedule
- ❐ agreeing on something we both want to do
- ❐ finding the time and energy
- ❐ contacting the right people to help us get started
- ❐ but what if the kids needed us?!
- ❐ I don't see any obstacles!

CARING / 15–45 Minutes / All Together

Leader: You have two options for this Caring time. One would be to bring the whole group back together for a time of prayer requests and prayer, as you have done in previous sessions. The other would be to follow the procedure below to share some appreciation for others in your group.

OPTION 1

Take time to share any prayer requests by answering the question below. Then close with a time of prayer, remembering the requests that have been shared. If you would like to pray in silence, say the word "Amen" when you have finished your prayer, so that the next person will know when to start.

"How can we help you in prayer this week?"

OPTION 2

You have probably been richly blessed by the people in your small group. Now is the time to tell them how they have blessed you.

Ask one person to sit in silence while the others go around and finish one of the sentences below about this person. Then, ask another person to remain silent while you go around again, etc.

- ❐ You have blessed me recently when you told the story about ...
- ❐ What inspires me most about your character is ...
- ❐ The aspect of your personality I would like to acquire into my own life is ...
- ❐ You have a way with people that I admire very much ...
- ❐ There is something about your faith in God that I really like ...
- ❐ I would use two of the following words to describe you because you are ...

accepting	encouraging	inspiring	sensitive
active	good-hearted	loyal	spontaneous
adventurous	growing	open	supportive
aware	helpful	productive	thoughtful
confident	authentic	real	tolerant
considerate	honest	righteous	vulnerable
creative	influential	risk-taking	warm

A New Spirituality

LIFE STORIES	BIBLE STUDY

PURPOSE

To introduce the subject of "A New Spirituality" and share your own stories.

AGENDA

 Gathering Study Caring

OPEN

 GATHERING / 15 Minutes / All Together

Leader: Welcome newcomers and explain the purpose and procedures in this course. Explain that this is the first of two sessions on the issue of "A New Spirituality."

Start off by reading the Introduction to the group or ask for a volunteer to read it. Then, use the Ice-Breaker to start the meeting. Remember to keep to the 3-part agenda.

INTRODUCTION

When we are young we have a tendency to be preoccupied with the material aspects of life. But as we mature we see more and more that the physical is not all there is to life. While we still feel there is much of life ahead, we realize that we are aging, and we start to think more of where life is headed, and what is beyond it. All of this leads us to consider our spiritual nature more and more. That means we need to work more on our connections—principally our connection with our Creator and God, but also our connections with the rest of life in God's Creation.

We will have two sessions on the issue of "A New Spirituality." In this session, the emphasis will be on sharing your own story. If you wish to spend another session on this topic and go deeper into this issue, you can choose to move to Track 2 for the next session ... or you can stay in Track 1 and go on to the next issue.

This is the first of two sessions on "A New Spirituality." Use the Ice-Breaker to get started.

Ice-Breaker: Home Remedy for a Fever. Go around the group on the first question. Then go around on the next question.

1. If your inner emotional state this past week could be measured with a thermometer, what would have been your temperature?
    - ❏ 98.6 degrees—Normal, healthy, alive!
    - ❏ 97.5 degrees—turning cold in the midst of stress and demands
    - ❏ 99.9 degrees—Probably no one noticed, but I've been a little out of sorts.
    - ❏ 102 degrees—Things have definitely been heating up inside of me.
    - ❏ 106 degrees—The stress is burning my brain, everything is hazy, and I'm not sure how I made it this far!

2. In the midst of what is happening inside of you, what has been your favorite "fever reducer" this past week?
    - ❏ encouragement from my spouse
    - ❏ a friend or friends who have listened
    - ❏ my prayer and devotional time
    - ❏ support from this group
    - ❏ my extended family
    - ❏ playing some of my favorite music
    - ❏ my time alone
    - ❏ watching my soaps and losing myself in the miseries of others
    - ❏ other _____

 ## STUDY / 30 Minutes / Groups of 4

Leader: If there are more than 7 in your group, we recommend that you subdivide into groups of 4 so that everyone can participate and you can finish the Study in 30 minutes.

Life Stories. Have someone read out loud the stories of the two people below. Then, use the questions to share some of your own experience.

Karl

All the time his children were in the home, Karl felt he had to be driven to achieve at his work. He had to achieve in order to provide for his family first of all, but he also felt he had to achieve in order to make sure his children were proud of him. When his youngest son graduated from college and took a job in another city, Karl went through a time of depression. He realized that at least in part it was because his work just didn't seem to have the meaning to him that it used to have. Then a friend invited him to a spiritual life retreat which included a lot of time in silent reflection, as well as times of sharing with others. He began to realize how his working to impress people, even his own children, was because as a child he never felt accepted by his father. He also began to understand, really for the first time, what he had heard before, that God was the Father whose love he didn't have to earn. With that realization came a new peace Karl had never known before.

Rose

Rose's only son died of AIDS last year when he was just short of 29 years old. She had been crushed when she learned that he was gay, but she always sought to be supportive to the end. Since that time she and her second husband have been working to build awareness of the needs of AIDS patients. But more and more Rose finds a disturbingly large number of people she gets close to dying, including other AIDS patients and friends her age with cancer. She has never considered herself to be "religious" before, but confronting death has also forced her to face some ultimate questions. She wants to believe that death is not the end, but she has always been a very rational person. She wonders if her new concern with this is just wishful thinking, or a valid exploration of something real.

DISCUSS

"There is no greater close-ness and inti-macy than when a couple opens their hearts to God together. Praying together enhances the completeness and oneness of a couple while it puts their differ-ences and adjustments in a better per-spective."
—H. Norman Wright in Romancing Your Marriage

Questions:

1. Which of the following comes closest to the view of God you had when you were in grade school?
    - [ ] a kindly old man—like George Burns
    - [ ] Santa Claus—without the red suit and reindeer
    - [ ] like my parent(s)
    - [ ] like Jesus—I saw God and Jesus as the same
    - [ ] a spirit—like Casper the friendly Ghost!
    - [ ] an angry man sending lightning bolts and punishing children
    - [ ] I had no concept of God.

2. Which of the following words would you associate most with God now? (Choose 3):

[ ] judge	[ ] guide	[ ] savior
[ ] creator	[ ] provider	[ ] powerful
[ ] parent	[ ] companion	[ ] all-knowing
[ ] life-source	[ ] mystery	[ ] angry
[ ] hidden	[ ] love	[ ] life-nurturer

3. If Rose were a friend of yours and came to you with her struggle, what would you most likely share with her?
    - [ ] "I've had those same feelings myself!"
    - [ ] why I choose to trust God's promises of eternal life
    - [ ] why I think it really is wishful thinking
    - [ ] "the plan of salvation"
    - [ ] I would share some good books I've read on this subject.
    - [ ] I wouldn't feel I had anything to share that would help.
    - [ ] other _____

4. What is the most spiritual experience you have shared with your spouse?
   - ❑ well, we were married in a church...
   - ❑ having a child together
   - ❑ going through a time of hardship and surviving
   - ❑ sharing in a mission or project for people in need
   - ❑ having our regular family devotions
   - ❑ attending church services together
   - ❑ a trip where we felt really in touch with the natural world
   - ❑ other _____

5. Karl was drawn to God by a void he felt that went back to his childhood; Rose was drawn by her need to make sense of the deaths of people close to her. What most draws you to God?
   - ❑ like Karl—my need for a caring heavenly Parent
   - ❑ like Rose—my need to believe something is beyond death
   - ❑ my need to believe there is a purpose to what happens in life
   - ❑ my need to believe in ultimate justice—good will be rewarded
   - ❑ my need for a Guide through the maze of life
   - ❑ my need to belong and feel connected to something larger than myself
   - ❑ my need to deal with the guilt in my life

6. What have you seen or experienced that gives you more confidence that you can find what you seek through God?
   - ❑ the promises of the Bible
   - ❑ the belief and experiences of my own parents
   - ❑ the way such a belief affects people I know in this group or in church
   - ❑ the way God seems to be working in my own life
   - ❑ just something about the way Jesus lived makes me believe it's all real
   - ❑ other _____

7. What do you most fear from being more spiritually involved?
   - ❑ being judged by hypocritical church people
   - ❑ loss of my independence and identity
   - ❑ being manipulated by religious frauds
   - ❑ having to give up my present lifestyle
   - ❑ nothing!
   - ❑ other _____

CARING / 15–45 Minutes / All Together

Leader: Regather all the groups of 4 back together. By this time in your group, you should know each other well enough to affirm one another with depth and insight. Start your Caring time with a little affirmation.

AFFIRMATION

The people in your group have special qualities which make your small group experience enriching: From the list below, choose a national park which best describes the person sitting on your left. Take turns telling the group what park you chose to describe the person sitting next to you:

GRAND CANYON NATIONAL PARK: What an impressive vista! You have character that has taken years of patient effort and constant attention.

GOLDEN GATE NATIONAL PARK: You bring people together and bridge the gap in a beautiful, stunning way.

SEQUOIA NATIONAL PARK: Your growth is so impressive that you reach into the skies and provide shade and security for many different creatures.

YOSEMITE NATIONAL PARK: You are the most popular choice for an exciting and adventurous experience!

MAMMOTH CAVE NATIONAL PARK: With hundreds of miles of underground passageways, you epitomize depth, mystery and hidden treasures.

STATUE OF LIBERTY NATIONAL MONUMENT: You are a living symbol to those around you of freedom, hope and a new life.

MOUNT RUSHMORE: You are an enduring testimony to leadership, character and integrity.

YELLOWSTONE NATIONAL PARK: With your hot springs and geysers you are a source of warmth for those who get close to you.

MOUNT RAINIER NATIONAL PARK: You keep people looking up and your high standards can be seen from a great distance.

THE ALAMO: You remind everyone who sees you of courage, tenacity and determination.

PRAYER

For the prayer time, stand in a circle, grab hands and take turns completing the sentence:

"Lord, I want to thank you for ..."

A New Spirituality

| LIFE STORIES | BIBLE STUDY |

PURPOSE

To go deeper into the subject of "A New Spirituality" and to look at a story in Scripture.

AGENDA

 Gathering   Study   Caring

OPEN

GATHERING / 15 Minutes / All Together

Leader: Welcome newcomers and explain the purpose and procedures of the group. Explain that this session is the second of two on the issue of "A New Spirituality."

The purpose of the Gathering time is to break the ice. Call time after 15 minutes and move on.

Ice Breaker: Scary Masks. Psychologists tell us that one reason children like to wear scary masks is the principle of "identification with the aggressor"—if they are afraid of ghosts, they won't be quite as afraid of them if they can dress up as a ghost and be one themselves. Or if they are afraid of a wild animal like a lion, they won't be quite as afraid if they can pretend they are that animal themselves. Adults have different fears.

Using the above principle, which of the following would you most like to dress up as?

❑ a dentist—with an evil grin and something that buzzes to stick in people's mouth!

❑ an auto mechanic —with greasy overalls and a recording that says, "We found a little problem" over and over again!

❑ a big clock—that runs so fast, everyone is always late!

❑ a college student—with a recording that says, "Send money! Send money! ..."

❑ "Father Time"—complete with a big mirror that magnifies your wrinkles!

❑ a police officer—complete with a light I can flash when I follow people!

❑ a smiling politician—with a recording that says "Trust me! Trust me! ..."

❑ other _____

Leader: If you have more than 7 in your group, we recommend subdividing into groups of 4 (4 at the dining table, 4 at the kitchen table, etc.) so that you can finish the Study in 30 minutes and everyone can participate. Be sure to save the last 15–45 minutes for the Caring time.

INTRODUCTION

Wrestling with God. In the following story Jacob is heading toward the land God had promised him and his descendants as the place for their future. On the way he wrestles alone with a man who ends up being not a man at all, but an angel of God. For the Israelite, that was the equivalent of encountering God himself. Jacob is wounded in the midst of this wrestling, which becomes a pivotal experience in his life, because it serves to clarify his life purpose, and gives him a new identity (the name "Israel" means "he struggles with God.") Many of us have to go through a similar time when we "wrestle" with God. As you look at the following story, think of what the nature is of your own "wrestling with God."

Have someone in your group read the story out loud. Then, go around on the first question and let anyone speak up. Then, go around on the next questions, etc. Be sure to save the last 15–45 minutes for the Caring time.

²²*That night Jacob got up and took his two wives, his two maidservants and his eleven sons and crossed the ford of the Jabbok.* ²³*After he had sent them across the stream, he sent over all his possessions.* ²⁴*So Jacob was left alone, and a man wrestled with him till daybreak.* ²⁵*When the man saw that he could not overpower him, he touched the socket of Jacob's hip so that his hip was wrenched as he wrestled with the man.* ²⁶*Then the man said, "Let me go, for it is daybreak."*

But Jacob replied, "I will not let you go unless you bless me."

²⁷*The man asked him, "What is your name?"*

"Jacob," he answered.

²⁸*Then the man said, "Your name will no longer be Jacob, but Israel, because you have struggled with God and with men and have overcome."*

²⁹*Jacob said, "Please tell me your name."*

But he replied, "why do you ask my name?" Then he blessed him there.

³⁰*So Jacob called the place Peniel, saying, "It is because I saw God face to face, and yet my life was spared."*

Genesis 32:22–30

1. What seems most significant to you in this story?
    - ❒ that Jacob had this experience when he was alone
    - ❒ that Jacob couldn't tell the difference at first between a messenger of God and an ordinary man
    - ❒ that this story seems to say it's okay to struggle with God
    - ❒ that God didn't kill Jacob for this!

2. Jacob encountered God in this unusual way during a period of aloneness. Where do you go to find time alone?
   - ❏ Good question—I don't!
   - ❏ I go in the "John" and lock the door!
   - ❏ I go out driving.
   - ❏ I go to my office.
   - ❏ I have this special little place out in nature.
   - ❏ I'm alone most of the time.

3. How do you relate to your times of aloneness?
   - ❏ I avoid them—I crave people!
   - ❏ When I'm alone I feel lonely.
   - ❏ I go right to the TV
   - ❏ I use them to get things done.
   - ❏ I use them to reflect or meditate.
   - ❏ I use them to read or listen to music.

4. When have you "wrestled with God"?
   - ❏ when I lost a loved one and I was angry with him
   - ❏ when things I had learned and experienced started me doubting
   - ❏ when I wasn't sure I wanted to be "the good little boy" or "good little girl" anymore
   - ❏ when I felt God calling me to him, and I wanted to go my own way
   - ❏ I wrestle with God all the time!
   - ❏ I've never had this kind of experience.

5. In your wrestling match with God right now, how do you see the match going?
   - ❏ He's got me in a "headlock."
   - ❏ He's lifted me above his head and spinning me in circles!—I don't know which way is up!
   - ❏ I think he's got me pinned!
   - ❏ We're countering each other's moves, and I think this match may well last to "daybreak"!
   - ❏ I'm fighting free from his grasp.
   - ❏ I've "thrown the match"—I was rooting for him anyway!

6. What blessing do you need from God to help you find healing?
   - ❏ assurance of his forgiveness
   - ❏ some indication that he really cares
   - ❏ direction to help put my life back together
   - ❏ courage to help me face myself honestly
   - ❏ faith to believe his promises

"I listen to more and more fifty-something men talk about their desire to deepen their relationship with God and walk closer to Him. Some are reconnecting after years of being disconnected. Others are seeking connection for the first time."
—Jim Smoke in *Facing 50: A View From the Mountaintop*

CARING / 15–45 Minutes / All Together

Leader: This course is drawing to a close. Start the decompression with this exercise.

SHARING

Sometimes it seems we don't get to see our small group members enough. Think about what you will miss about the group after this course is finished. Take turns sharing with your group what came to mind.

PRAYER

Close with a time of prayer and thanksgiving.

<table>
<tr><td>

</td><td colspan="2">

A New Future
</td></tr>
<tr><td></td><td>LIFE STORIES</td><td>BIBLE STUDY</td></tr>
</table>

PURPOSE

To introduce the issue of "A New Future" and to share your appreciation for each other.

AGENDA

 Gathering   Study   Caring

OPEN

 GATHERING / 15 Minutes / All Together

Leader: Welcome any newcomers. Keep in mind that this is the last session or the next to the last session in this course. If you are using the short course, be sure to save some time for the group evaluation at the close of the session. You will find this on pages 75–76.

If you have one more session, take some time at the close of this session to plan a celebration at the end of the next session.

INTRODUCTION

Doing the same old things in the same old ways gets tiring after a while for most people. That is why it's so great that in each stage of life God presents us with new opportunities and new challenges. This is as true for the person facing the empty nest as it is for the young person striking out for the first time on their own. That is the exciting thing about serving a living God—we can always look forward to the future with hope, because we know that God always has new and exciting things in store!

Our new future will only be all it can be if we first let go of the past, so that we do not try to recreate our future in the likeness of our past. Letting go is always the hard part. But for the one who has the faith to let go, God always provides so much more.

We will have two sessions on the issue of our "New Future" as empty nesters. In this session, the emphasis will be on sharing your own story. If you wish to spend another session on this topic and go deeper into this issue, you can choose to move to Track 2 for your final session.

This is the first of two sessions on "A New Future." Use the Ice-Breaker to get started.

Ice-Breaker: Assessing the Future. Go around and let each person answer one of the questions below, or both.

1.   Which phrase would best describe your philosophy about facing the future?
     ❒ "I don't want to grow up!"
     ❒ "Back to the Future!"
     ❒ "You can't go home again."
     ❒ "One day at a time, Sweet Jesus."
     ❒ "He who isn't busy being born is busy dying."
     ❒ "The future belongs to those who plan for it."
     ❒ "I don't know what the future holds, but I know who holds the future."
     ❒ "Every day in every way, things are getting better."
     ❒ "The future's so bright, I've got to wear shades!"

2.   Finish this sentence: "One thing that I'll have in the future which I did not have in the past is ..."

STUDY / 30 Minutes / Groups of 4

Leader: If you have more than 7 in your group, divide into groups of 4 where everyone can participate. If this is the last session in this course (if you are using the reduced schedule) save time at the close to evaluate this course, using the questions on pages 75–76.

Life Stories. Have someone read aloud the stories of the two people below. Then, use the questions to share some of your own experience.

Sharon
Shortly after Sharon's youngest son went off to college, her husband filed for divorce. Sharon felt she had lost everything that was important to her. But as she began to find healing from her loss, she began to see that she had the ability to help other women who were going through what she had gone through. She also heard of a seminary that had a special weekend for women considering the ministry. When she was younger she had considered professional ministry, but thought that it didn't seem to be a very viable option at the time for a woman. Now new possibilities seemed to be opening up, just as she was discovering her own skills at helping others. She attended the special weekend program, and as she entered the seminary doors she felt like a kid again.

Norm
Norm had a very special relationship with his daughter Karen. Karen had been a tomboy who had always gone fishing with him, and who talked

very easily to him. Norm never felt any of the boys she dated in high school or college were good enough for her, including the one she ended up marrying. He was depressed for some time after she left the home. Things just weren't the same. But when Karen started having children of her own, Norm discovered a new joy in his life—grandchildren! Not only were they enjoyable on their own right, but watching his daughter mature as a mother brought a new sense of pleasure and completion to his life.

Questions:

1. What have you experienced recently which, like Sharon's going to seminary, made you feel "like a kid again"?
   ❑ like Sharon—returning to school
   ❑ being with my grandchildren
   ❑ an especially romantic evening with my spouse
   ❑ going to an amusement park
   ❑ taking on a new challenge
   ❑ watching a ball game
   ❑ other _____

2. In what experience do you most strongly relate to the people in the stories above?
   ❑ having felt like I lost everything at one point, like Sharon
   ❑ learning I could help others going through what I've experienced, like Sharon
   ❑ starting a new career in mid-life, like Sharon
   ❑ feeling depressed when a child I was especially close to left home, like Norm
   ❑ discovering new joy in life through my grandchildren, like Norm
   ❑ enjoying seeing my adult child mature as a parent, like Norm

3. What from your past is hardest for you to leave behind?
   ❑ my role as a parent
   ❑ my youth
   ❑ my former profession
   ❑ the romance of our young married years
   ❑ the time when my parents were healthy and I got to be the kid
   ❑ other _____

4. If you could assign a color to your future, what color would you choose?
   - ☐ black!—There's nothing there.
   - ☐ gray—dull and unexciting
   - ☐ fiery orange—full of conflict, but also the power of fire
   - ☐ yellow—full of warmth
   - ☐ sky blue—peaceful and serene
   - ☐ purple—rich and exciting

5. What is your dream for the future now?

6. What help do you need to bring your dream to a reality?
   - ☐ someone to encourage me to let go of the past so I can grasp my future
   - ☐ someone to pray with me and encourage me
   - ☐ someone with expertise in the area of _____
   - ☐ someone to just tell me that my dream isn't crazy!
   - ☐ other _____

CARING / 15–45 Minutes / All Together

Leader: Regather everyone back together. If this is the last session, use the evaluation on pages 75–76 to evaluate the course. If you have one more session, use some of the time to plan a party for the close of the last session. If this is your final session, you may want to follow the Caring activities in Session 13.

AFFIRMATION

Every Christian reflects the character of Jesus in some way. As your group has gotten to know each other, you can begin to see how each person demonstrates Christ in their very own personality.

Ask one person to sit in silence while the others share one way in which this person reminds you of Jesus. Then, go around again on the next person, etc.

You remind me of ...

- ☐ JESUS THE HEALER: You seem to be able to touch someone's life and bind their wounds and help make them whole.

- ☐ JESUS THE SERVANT: There seems to be nothing that you wouldn't do for someone.

70

☐ JESUS THE PREACHER: You have a way of sharing your faith that is provoking, inspiring and full of hope.

☐ JESUS THE ADMINISTRATOR: As Jesus had a plan for the disciples, you are able to organize to accomplish great things for God.

☐ JESUS THE REBEL: By doing the unexpected you remind me of Jesus' way of revealing God in unique, surprising ways.

☐ JESUS THE TEACHER: You have a way of bringing the Scripture to life in a way that offers hope and truth.

☐ JESUS THE CRITIC: You have the courage to say what needs to be said, even if it isn't always popular.

☐ JESUS THE LEADER: Because you are a visionary, people would be willing to follow you anywhere.

☐ JESUS THE SACRIFICE: Like Jesus, you seem to be willing to sacrifice anything to glorify God.

☐ JESUS THE MIRACLE WORKER: You seem to defy the laws of nature in your efforts to make God's kingdom come alive.

PRAYER

Close with a time of prayer, asking for God's help in our continued healing and in our commitment to celebrate life.

A New Future

LIFE STORIES	BIBLE STUDY

PURPOSE

To finish this course, to celebrate what you have experienced together, and to decide about the future.

AGENDA

 Gathering Study Caring

OPEN

 GATHERING / 15 Minutes / All Together

Leader: Work backwards on the meeting plan. Decide how much time you need for the group evaluation at the close. Then, set aside time for the Study. The remaining time you can spend in this meaningful and affirming Gathering time.

Tell-Tale Fairy Tales. Let one person answer one or both of the questions below. Then, go on to the next person and around the group.

1. Which of the following myths or fairy tales best expresses what has happened to you since this group began?
    ❑ Sleeping Beauty—This group has awakened a beauty in me.
    ❑ Cinderella—It's been great, but now it's midnight ... .
    ❑ Humpty-Dumpty—"All the King's horses and all the King's men (or women!) couldn't have put me together again."
    ❑ The Wizard of Oz—We've been to Oz together and found all the love and courage and knowledge we needed.
    ❑ Pandora's Box—I fear we have just opened it!!
    ❑ Pinocchio—The group has helped me confront my lies.
    ❑ Peter Pan—I can fly! I can fly!

2. What part of this "fairy-tale" would you most want to "re-read" or re-experience?

STUDY / 30 Minutes / Groups of 4

Leader: Break into groups of 4 if you have more than 7 in your group. Be sure to save the last 15–45 minutes for the evaluation at the close of this meeting.

INTRODUCTION

Striking Out Into a New Land. The story of Abraham (originally called Abram), Father of the nation of Israel, serves as a stirring example of one who was willing to let go of a secure, known past, and strike out into the unfamiliar land of the future. God told him to go to a new land. He didn't have the chance to fly out ahead of time and check the job situation or the real estate market. He just went because God called him to do so. And because of his faithfulness, Abraham became father of a nation. The land of our future can be just as dark and uncertain as the foreign land to which Abraham journeyed, but it is the land to which God calls us, and he promises to be there with us.

Have someone in your group read the passage out loud. Then go around on the first question and let everyone speak up. Then go around again on the next question, etc.

12 *The Lord had said to Abram, "Leave your country, your people and your father's household and go to the land I will show you.*

²"I will make you into a great nation
and I will bless you;
I will make your name great,
and you will be a blessing.
³I will bless those who bless you,
and whoever curses you I will curse;
and all peoples on earth
will be blessed through you."

⁴So Abram left, as the Lord had told him; and Lot went with him. Abram was seventy-five years old when he set out from Haran. ⁵He took his wife Sarai, his nephew Lot, all the possessions they had accumulated and the people they had acquired in Haran, and they set out for the land of Canaan, and they arrived there.

⁶Abram traveled through the land as far as the site of the great tree of Moreh at Shechem. At that time the Canaanites were in the land. ⁷The Lord appeared to Abram and said, "To your offspring I will give this land." So he built an altar there to the Lord, who had appeared to him.

Genesis 12:1–7

1. Had you been Abram, how would you have most likely responded to God's call to move?
   - ❑ "Pull up roots?—mine run too deep!"
   - ❑ "Prove to me it's really you—and then, maybe ..."
   - ❑ "Could I just go on ahead and check this place out first?"
   - ❑ "Travel?—of course! How exciting!"
   - ❑ "If you say so, God—I'll stick my neck out."

2. Of the things Abram had to leave, what would be the hardest for you to leave?
   - ❑ his country—the area where you now live, with its familiarity
   - ❑ his people—friends and the people of your neighborhood
   - ❑ his father's household—your extended family, including adult children living in the area

3. Which of the blessings that Abram was promised would have been most important to you?
   - ❑ "make you into a great nation"—to have a lot of descendants who look to you as patriarch or matriarch
   - ❑ "make your name great"—to become famous
   - ❑ "bless those who bless you"—to have good things happen to my friends and family
   - ❑ "all peoples on earth will be blessed through you"—to make a real, visible difference in this world
   - ❑ "to your offspring I will give this land"—to have material plenty

4. What is the nature of the land God is calling you to leave behind to reach out for the Promised Land of your future?

5. What promised blessing would make it easier for you to leave that land behind?
   - ❑ to know it would help my family
   - ❑ to know it would help me realize my potential
   - ❑ to know it would make me better off materially
   - ❑ to know it would help me make a difference in this world
   - ❑ to know it would help me be closer to God through my obedience

6. What help do you need from God or others to "strike out for your Promised Land"?

"We cannot live our lives constantly looking back, listening back, lest we be turned to pillars of longing and regret ..."
—Frederick Buechner in *The Sacred Journey*

74

CARING / 15–45 Minutes / All Together

Leader: Bring all the groups back together. Evaluate your group experience and decide about the future. Then you may want to plan a special time of prayer to conclude this course.

EVALUATION

Take a few minutes to look back over your experience and reflect. Go around on each point and finish the sentences.

1. As I see it, our purpose and goal as a group was to:

2. We achieved our goal(s):
   - ❒ completely
   - ❒ almost completely
   - ❒ somewhat
   - ❒ We blew it.

3. The high point in this course for me has been:
   - ❒ the Scripture exercises
   - ❒ the sharing
   - ❒ discovering myself
   - ❒ the fun of the fellowship
   - ❒ belonging to a real community of love
   - ❒ finding new energy and purpose for my life

4. One of the most significant ways I have grown is:

5. In my opinion, our group functioned:
   - ❒ smoothly, and we grew
   - ❒ pretty well, but we didn't grow
   - ❒ It was tough, but we grew.
   - ❒ It was tough, and we didn't grow.

6. The thing I appreciate most about the group as a whole is:

CONTINUATION

Do you want to continue as a group? If so, what do you need to improve? Finish the sentence:

"If I were to suggest one thing we could do to improve our group, it would be ... "

MAKE A COVENANT

A covenant is a promise made to each other in the presence of God. Its purpose is to indicate your intention to make yourselves available to one another for the fulfillment of the purposes you share. In a spirit of prayer, work your way through the following sentences, trying to reach an agreement on each statement pertaining to your ongoing life together. Write out your covenant like a contract, stating your purpose, goals, and the ground rules for your group.

1. The purpose of our group will be ... (finish the sentence)

2. Our goals will be:

3. We will meet for _____weeks, after which we will decide if we wish to continue as a group.

4. We will meet from _____ to _____ and we will strive to start on time and end on time.

5. We will meet at _____ (place) or we will rotate from house to house.

CURRICULUM

If you decide to continue as a group for a few more weeks, what are you going to use for study and discipline? There are several other studies available at this 201 Series level. 301 Courses, designed for deeper Bible study with study notes, are also available.

For more information about small group resources and possible direction, please contact your small group coordinator or SERENDIPITY at 1-800-525-9563.

Studies From the Old Testament

1. Abraham Tested With Isaac (Gen. 22:1–19)
    Consider what it means to turn your adult child over to God,
    putting him or her into God's hands.

2. Crossing the Sea (Exo. 14:21–31)
    Focus on the "Red Sea" transitions in your life.

3. Balaam's Donkey and the Angel (Num. 22:21–35)
    Consider God's direction of you when your life has to take a "mid-
    course correction."

4. Joshua Renews the Covenant (Joshua 24:1–27)
    Consider what it means to renew your own covenant with God at
    this transitional stage of your life.

5. Gideon's Fear, Faith and Fleece (Judges 6:1–40)
    Look at what it means to find God's will for your future.

6. Isaiah's Vision (Isaiah 6:1–13)
    Consider where God is calling you to say, "Here am I, send me!"
    as you look at your future life purpose.

7. Valley of the Dry Bones (Ezekiel 37:1–14)
    Reflect on how God can bring you personal renewal when you
    feel everything truly "alive" is in the past.

Studies From the New Testament

1. Do Not Worry (Matt. 6:25–34)
    Consider what it means to hand your anxieties about an unsure
    future over to God.

2. Jesus Walks on Water (Matt. 14:22–36)
    Look at the risks God may be calling you to take to take hold of
    the future.

3. Parable of the Talents (Matt. 25:14–30)
    Take a look at the talents God has given you, in order to consid-
    er what God may be asking you to do with those talents in your
    future.

4. Gethsemane (Mark 14:32–42)
    Learn how to find and accept God's will for your future as you look
    at how Christ struggled with God's will for him.

5. Parable of the Rich Fool (Luke 12:13–21)
   Consider your priorities as you think of how you want to be remembered in life.

6. The Rich Ruler and Eternal Life (Luke 18:18–30)
   Think of what eternal life means to you in relation to the things that pass away.

7. Raising of Lazarus (John 11:1–44)
   Think through what it means to grieve what is lost, and how Christ always brings to life something new.

RESOURCES FOR FURTHER STUDY

Gerber, Jerry, Janet Wolff, Walter Klores and Gene Brown. *Lifetrends: The Future of Baby Boomers and Other Aging Americans.* New York: Macmillan, 1989.
   • This is an excellent resource for those wanting to explore the challenges and resources for people as they age in the future.

Gilligan, Carol. *In a Different Voice: Psychological Theory and Women's Development.* Cambridge: Harvard University Press, 1982.
   • This is a reaction to Levinson's work, showing how one's psychological development through various age periods is different for women.

Levinson, Daniel. *The Seasons of a Man's Life.* New York: Ballantine Books, 1978.
   • This is a modern classic on the changes a man goes through as he traverses different age periods.

Sheehy, Gail. *Passages.* New York: E. P. Dalton, 1976.
   • A popular adaptation of Levinson's earlier studies of adult development.

Smoke, Jim. *Facing 50: A View From the Mountaintop.* Nashville: Thomas Nelson Publishers, 1994.
   • This book has good input, written from a Christian perspective, on facing the challenges of this age period, including grandparenting, helping with aging parents and vocational crises.